WINNING CHESS TACTICS FOR JUNIORS

534 ONE- TWO- AND THREE- MOVE COMBINATIONS FOR THE DEVELOPING CHESSPLAYER

(Based on the bestselling tactical training guide, COMBINATION CHALLENGE!)

Edited by Lou Hays

HAYS PUBLISHING PARK HILL, OKLAHOMA

Editor: Lou Hays
Book Design and Typeset: Lou Hays
Final Proof: Sid Pickard
Diagrams electronically created on "Diagram 2.0."

PRINTED IN THE UNITED STATES OF AMERICA

Reprinted 2011

Hays Publishing
P.O. Box 777
Park Hill, Oklahoma 74451

ISBN 1-880673-93-2 Softcover

Dedicated to
the faculty and chess students of
Walnut Hill Elementary, Dallas, Texas
with special thanks to
Linda Draganchuk and Judy Zimney

EXPLANATION OF SYMBOLS

1.	WHITE TO PLAY AND WIN
1...	BLACK TO PLAY AND WIN
!	STRONG MOVE
!!	VERY STRONG MOVE
?	WEAK MOVE
??	BLUNDER
+	CHECK
+-+	DOUBLE CHECK
#	CHECKMATE
e.p.	CAPTURES *EN PASSANT*
x	CAPTURES

TABLE OF CONTENTS

IMPROVING YOUR CHESS RAPIDLY THROUGH TACTICS TRAINING

Winning Chess Tactics for Juniors is derived from the best-selling tactical guide Combination Challenge! — with two very important differences — (a) Winning Chess Tactics for Juniors is made up only of problems with one-two-and three-move solutions, and (b) It is priced with the junior chessplayer in mind. Although the solutions are all short, the diagrams are NOT necessarily easy. If your game is lacking tactically, nothing will be more beneficial to you RIGHT NOW than devouring as many of these diagrams as possible for the next few months. Pattern recognition is the key to improving your chess at this stage in your chess career. Once you get your rating to the 1750 or 1800 level, you will be ready to move on to *Combination Challenge!* and other more advanced tactics books. In order to improve your tactical ability and learn to play sharp, tactical chess the following system of study is recommended:

A) TRY TO SPEND SOME TIME EVERY DAY WORKING ON THE DIAGRAMS. At the rate of 20 diagrams per day you can go through the book in just under a month.

B) SOLVE DIRECTLY FROM THE BOOK, NOT ON YOUR CHESSBOARD. This is slightly more difficult, but will help your visualization ability. Use your board and pieces only on the diagrams you cannot work in your head.

C) DO NOT SPEND MORE THAN 5 MINUTES AT A TIME ON ANY ONE DIAGRAM. Some of these solutions are more challenging than others. If you have no idea of the solution to a diagram after 5 minutes, it is better to look up the answer and get the right idea into your head instead of becoming frustrated and wasting valuable time. The concept is to see as many diagrams and solutions as you can in the shortest period of time possible, not force yourself to endure a gruesome exam every day. Diagram training is learning by repetition, a sort of "osmosis." You will, after examining enough positions, begin to develop a "feel" for tactics. Do not worry about how much you are or are not learning as you go. Just continue a steady diet of diagrams and you will rapidly begin to see and use these patterns in your own games. A significant rise in strength and rating should follow.

D) EACH TIME YOU GO THROUGH THE BOOK, PLACE A CHECK BY THE DIAGRAM IF YOU ANSWER IT CORRECTLY. You will notice a small 1_ 2_ and 3_ between each pair of diagrams. As you go through the book for the first time place a check in the 1_ space if you answer correctly. Leave it blank if you cannot find the answer within 5 minutes. After looking up the solution and seeing it in your head, move on to the next problem. When you go through the book a second time, again place a check by each diagram you successfully solve, only this time place a mark in the 2_ area. The third time you study the book you will make your checks in the 3_ area. By using this method you can accurately track your progress, concentrate on your weaknesses, and watch yourself getting better and better each time you go through the book. Remember, solving diagrams is FUN — a most pleasant way to improve your chess. Make the start now and ENJOY this book.

DISCOVERY

The discovery is one of the most powerful types of move possible in a game of chess. The term "discovery" simply means that a piece is moved from a rank, file, or diagonal while uncovering an attack by friendly forces behind it on the line, thereby giving both pieces a chance to simultaneously threaten the opponent. Discoveries come in three varieties. The most powerful is the DOUBLE CHECK, in which the moving piece gives check and uncovers a check on the enemy King by another piece. It is easy to analyze the response to double check: The attacked King must move. Interposition or capture of a checking piece are not possible. DISCOVERED CHECK means that the enemy King is attacked only by the piece unleashed along the line (file, rank, or diagonal), while the moving or discovering piece is free to make threats of its own. DISCOVERED ATTACK occurs in the same manner as the others, except that the enemy King is not directly involved. Discovered attacks of any kind are extremely dangerous and even the threat of a discovered check or double check often brings a chess game to a sudden end. Watch for all three types of discovery in this chapter.

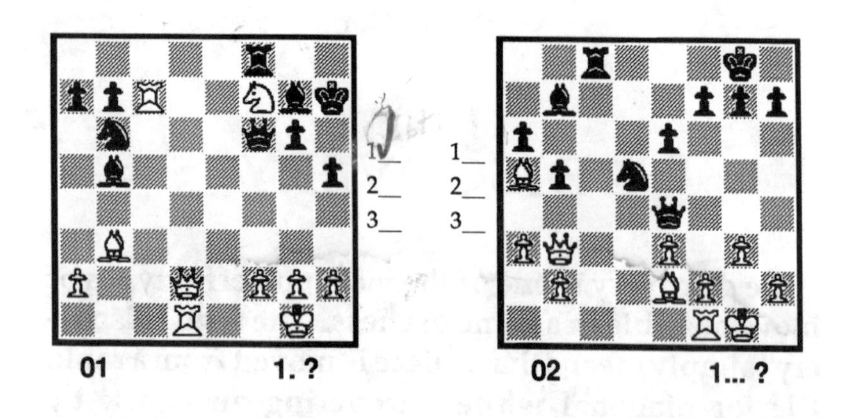

01 1. ?

02 1... ?

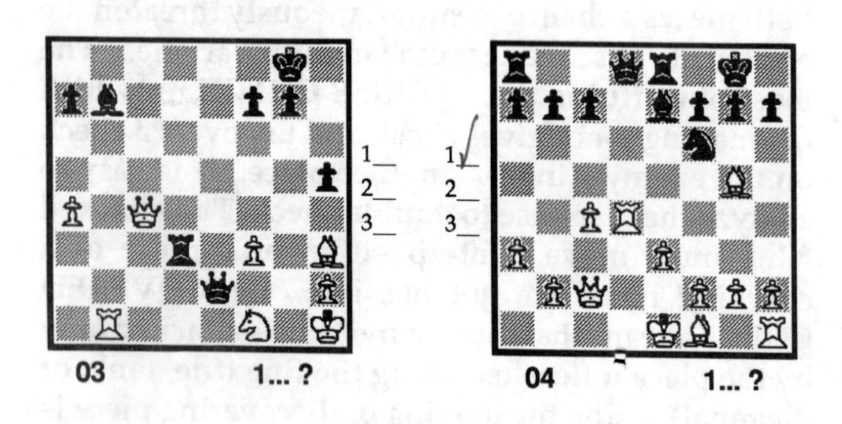

03 1... ?

04 1... ?

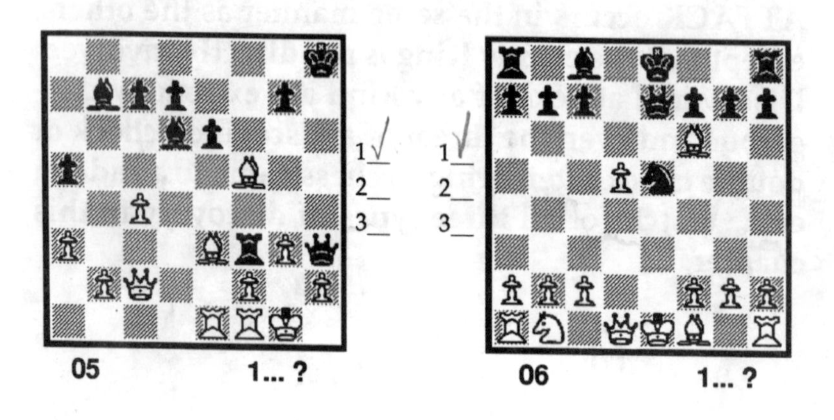

05 1... ?

06 1... ?

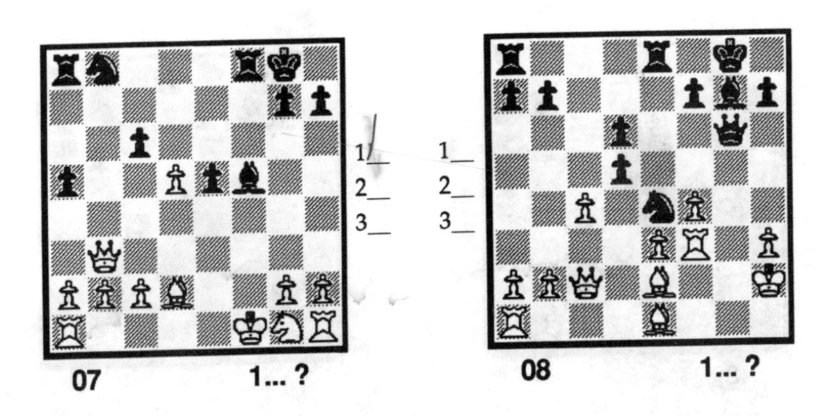

07 1... ?

08 1... ?

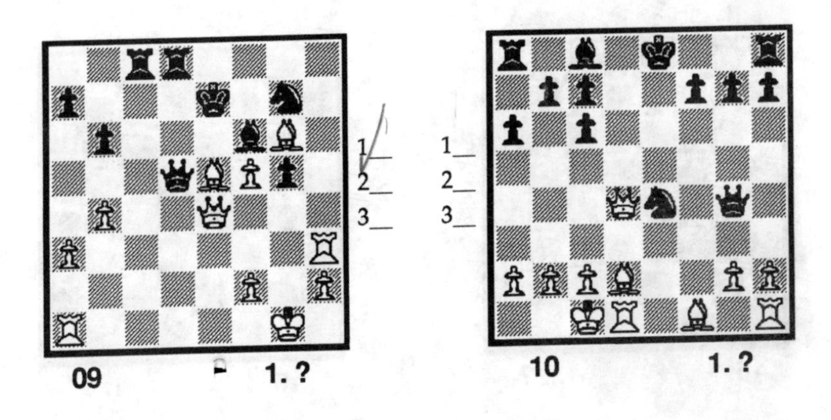

09 1. ?

10 1. ?

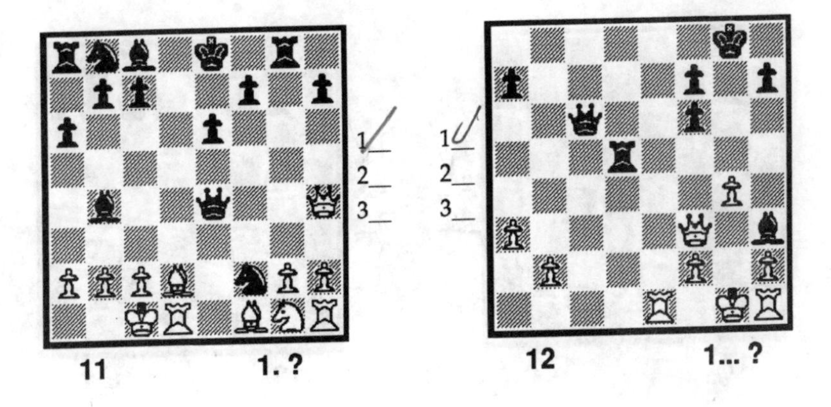

11 1. ?

12 1... ?

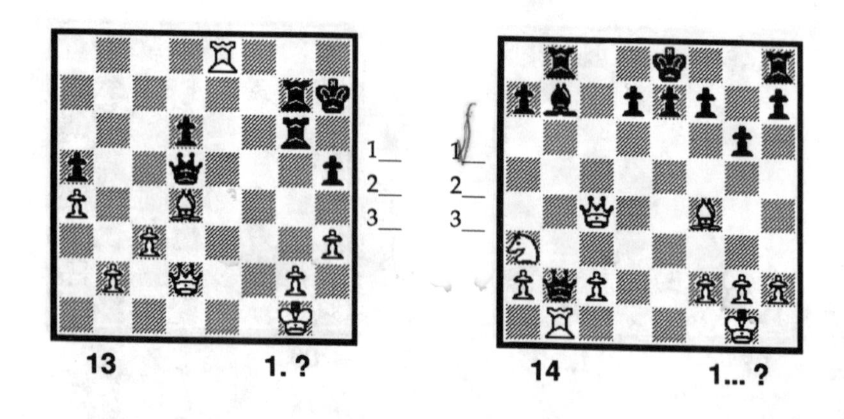

13 1. ?

14 1... ?

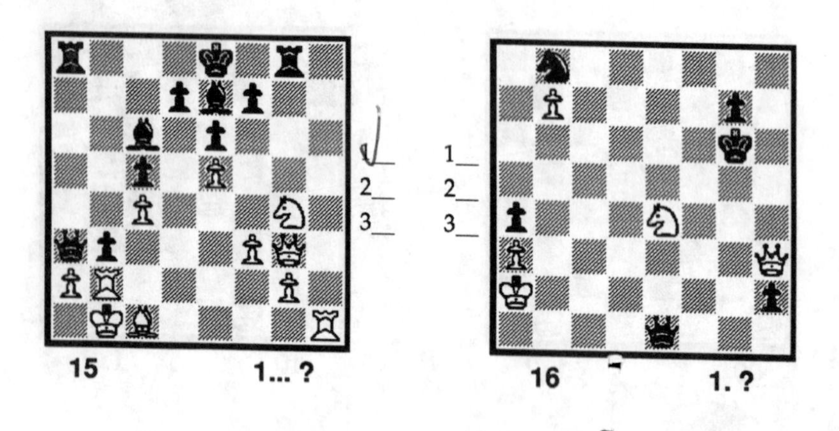

15 1... ?

16 1. ?

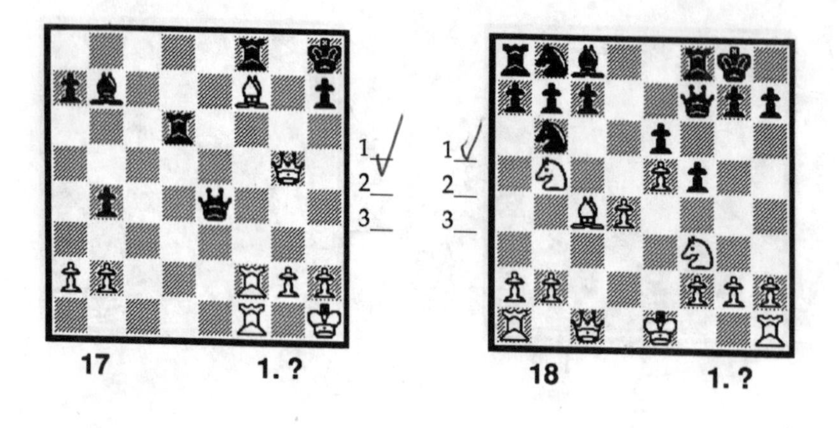

17 1. ?

18 1. ?

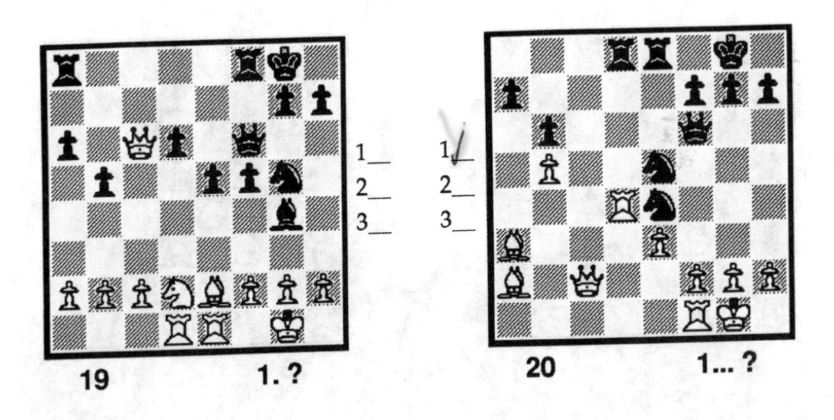

19 1. ?

20 1... ?

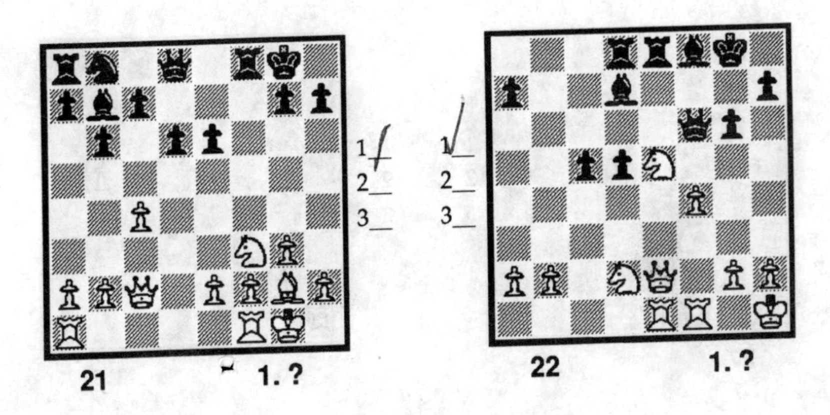

21 1. ?

22 1. ?

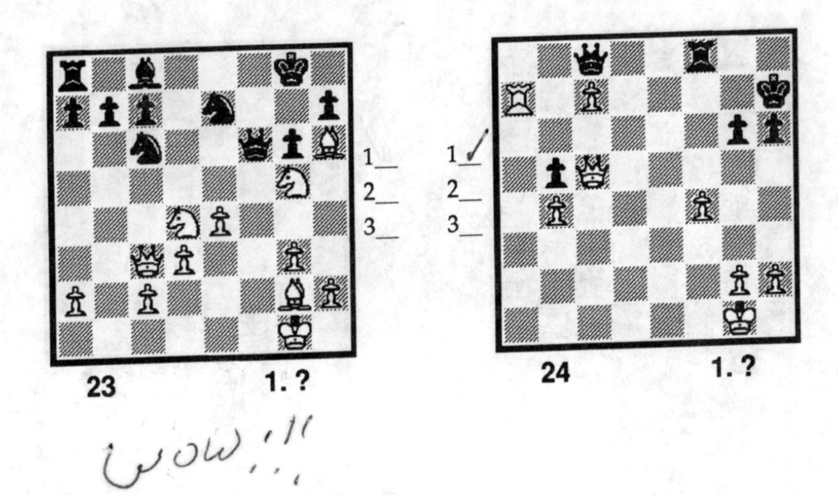

23 1. ?

24 1. ?

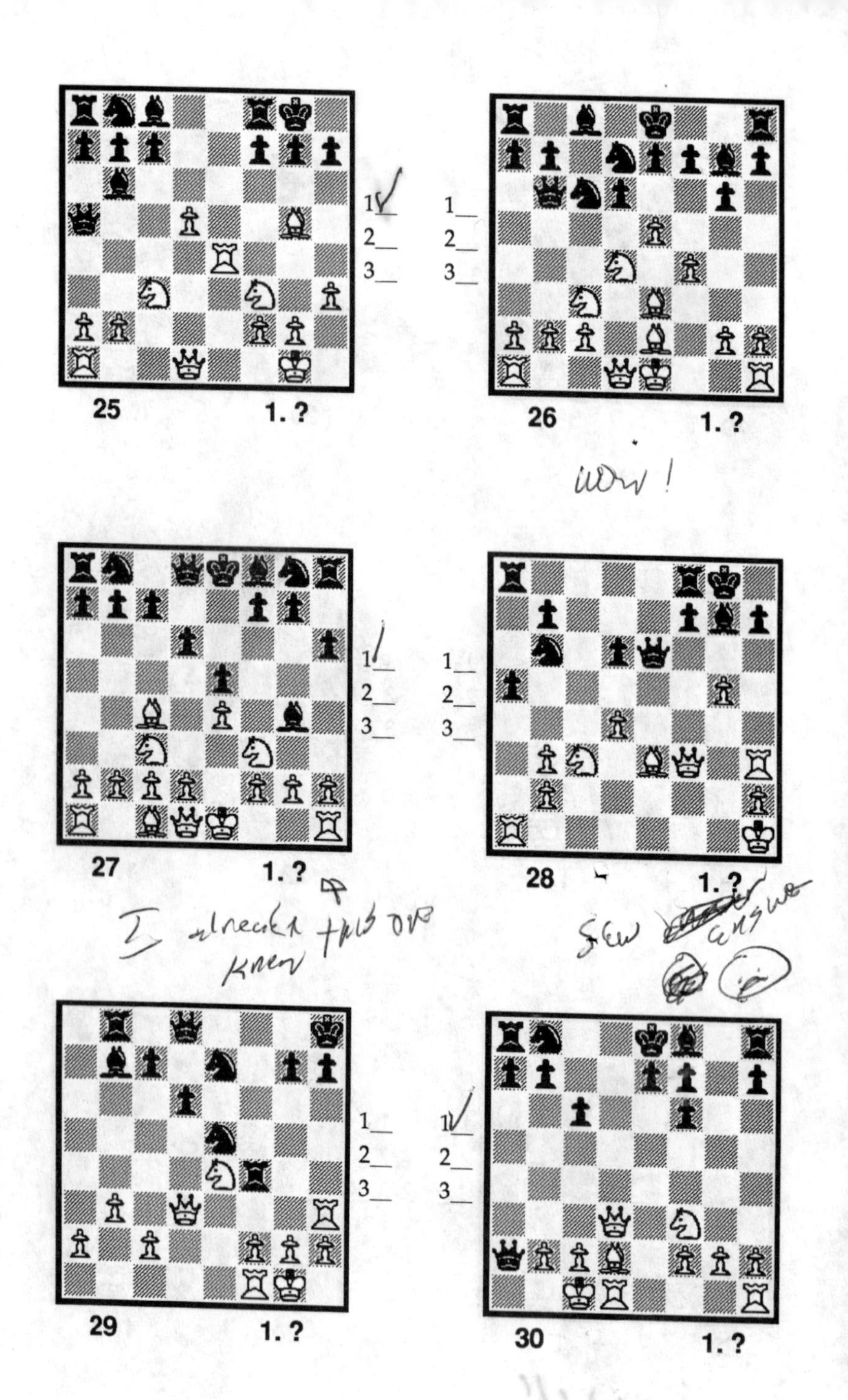
25
1. ?
1__
2__
3__
26
1. ?
27
1. ?
28
1. ?
29
1. ?
30
1. ?

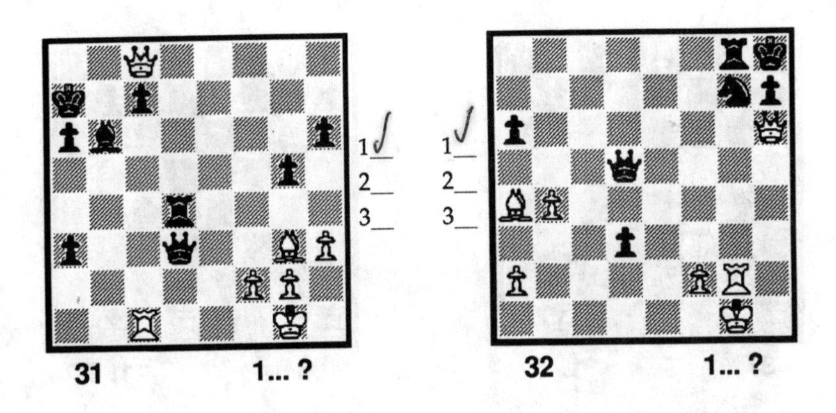

31 1... ?

32 1... ?

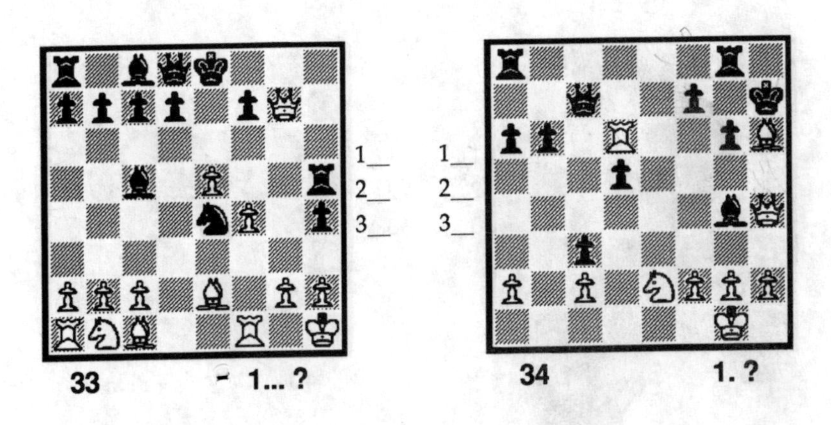

33 1... ?

34 1. ?

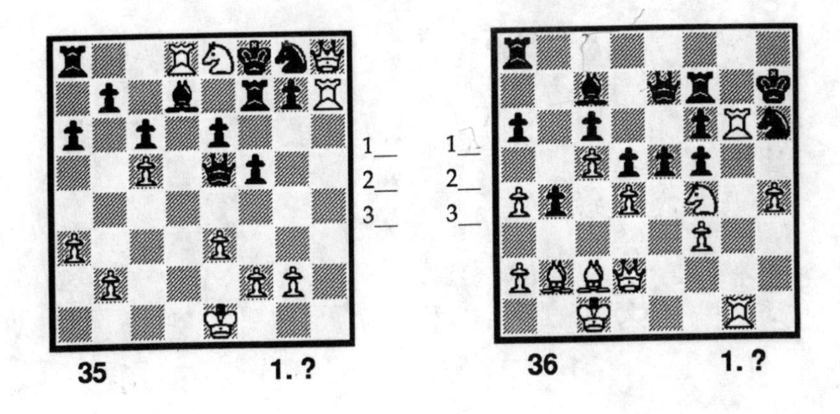

35 1. ?

36 1. ?

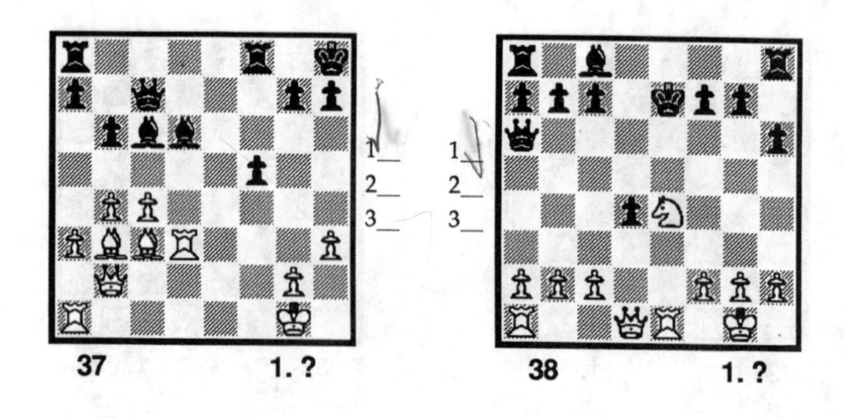

37 1. ?

38 1. ?

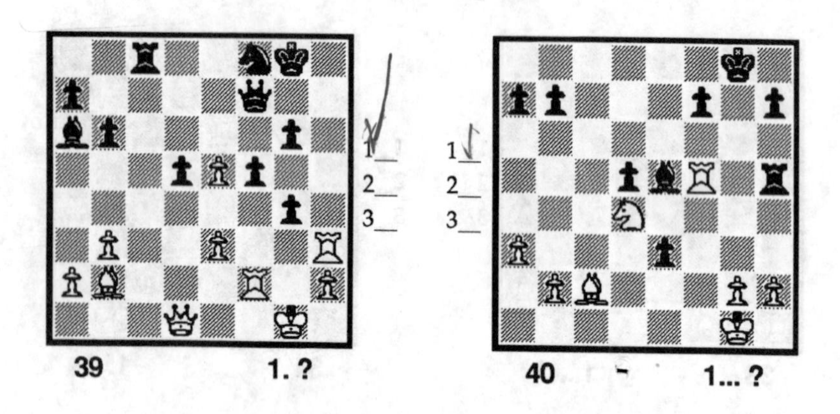

39 1. ?

40 1... ?

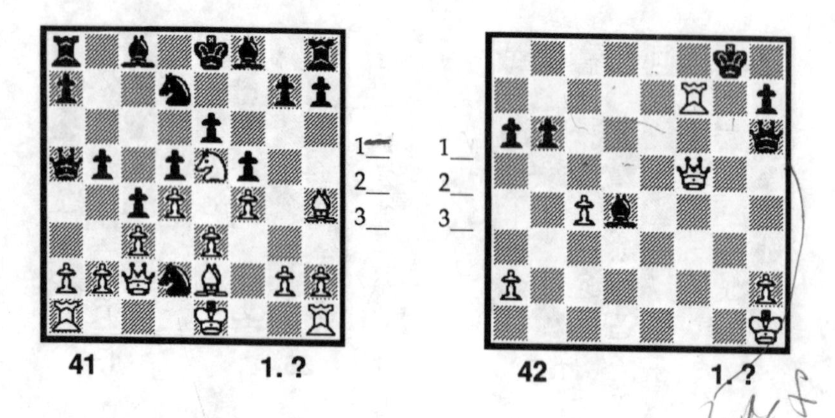

41 1. ?

42 1. ?

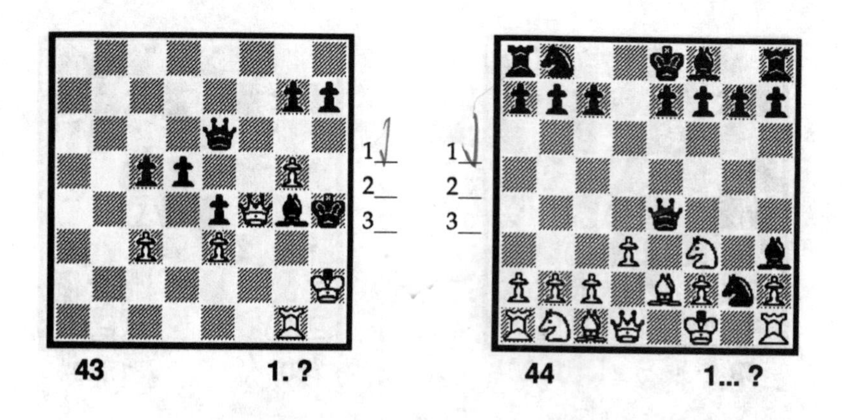

43 **1. ?**

44 **1... ?**

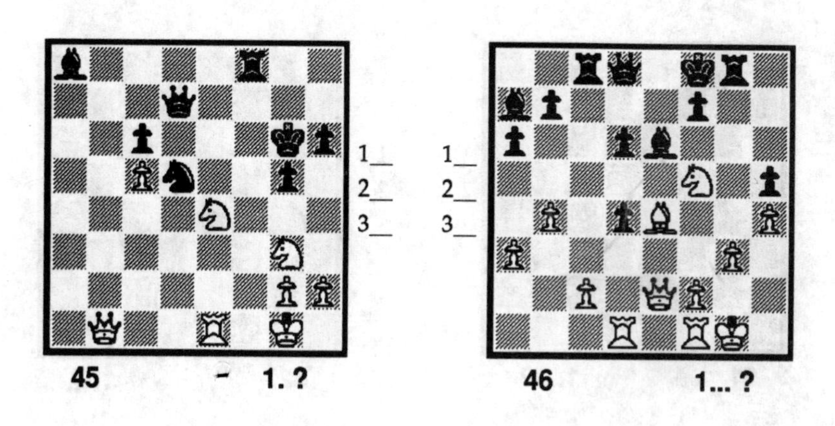

45 **1. ?**

46 **1... ?**

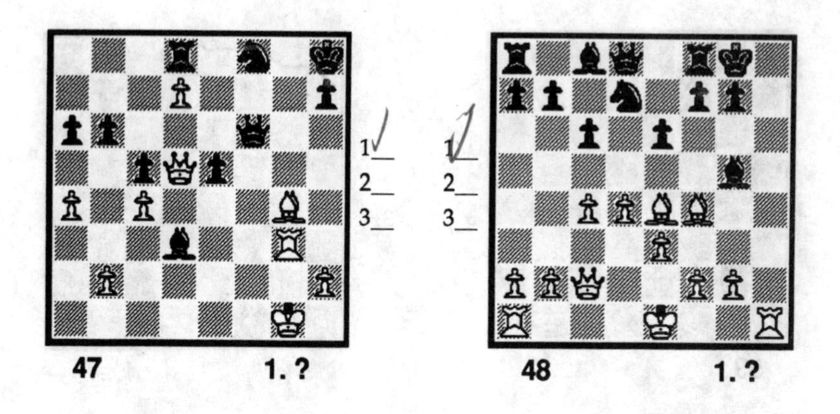

47 **1. ?**

48 **1. ?**

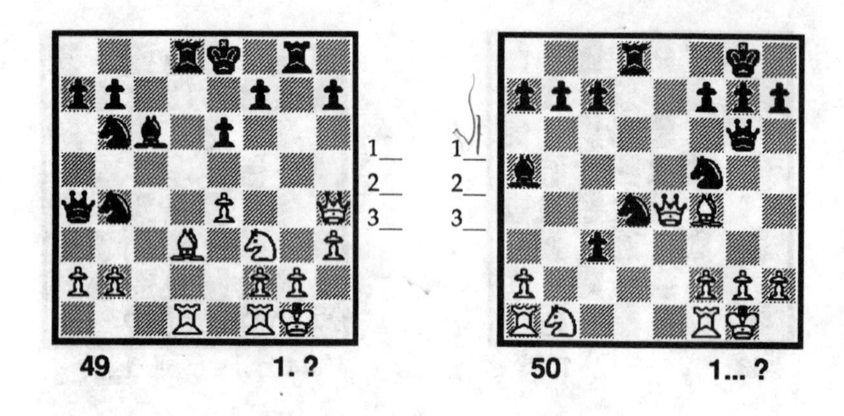
1__
2__
3__
1__
2__
3__
49
1. ?
50
1... ?

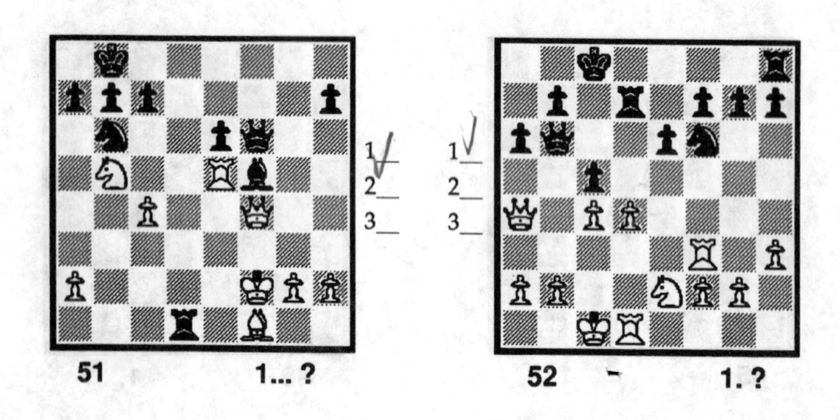
1__
2__
3__
1__
2__
3__
51
1... ?
52
1. ?

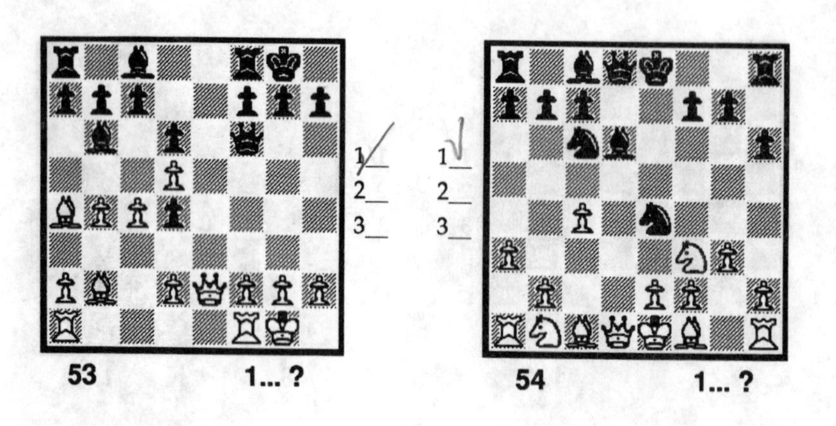
1__
2__
3__
1__
2__
3__
53
1... ?
54
1... ?

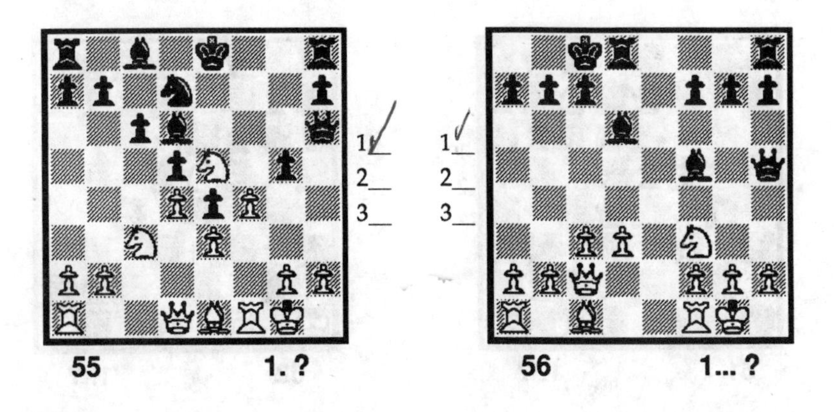

55 1. ?

56 1... ?

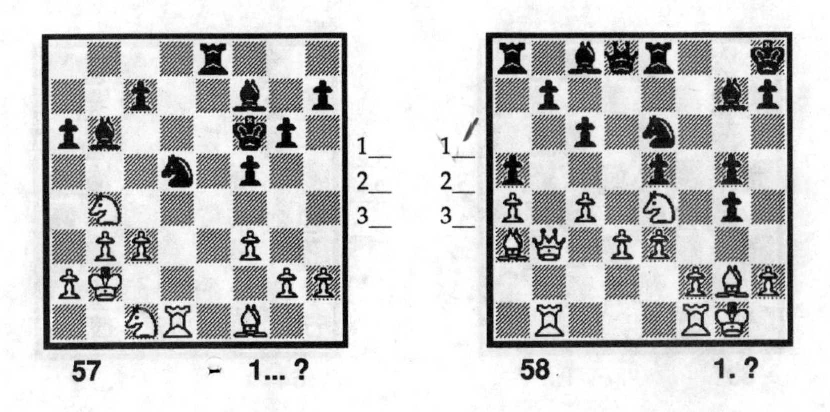

57 1... ?

58 1. ?

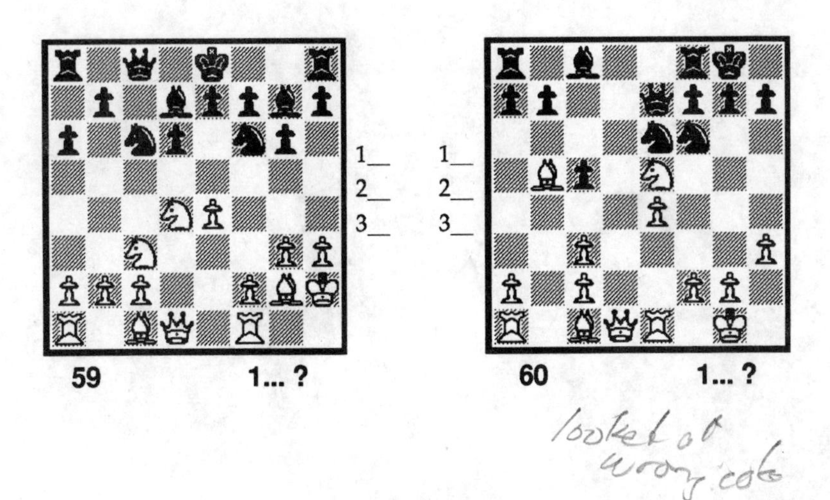

59 1... ?

60 1... ?

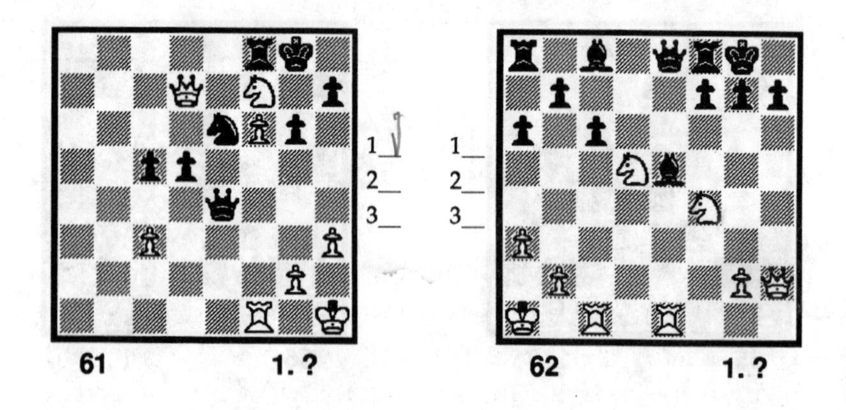

61 1. ?

62 1. ?

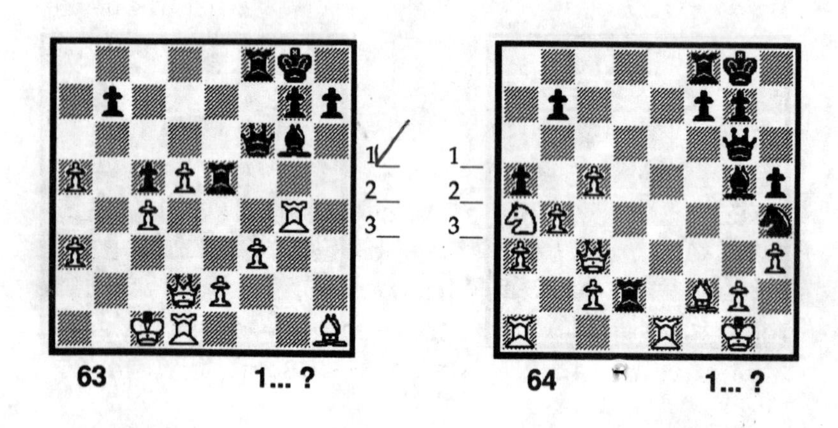

63 1... ?

64 1... ?

CHAPTER 2

QUEEN SACRIFICE

Surely every chessplayer has dreamed of that classic moment in chess - the Queen sacrifice. Giving up the strongest piece on the board in a sweeping and often totally unexpected fashion is associated with some of the most impressive victories ever recorded. Usually the Queen sacrifice occurs as the crowning effort of a well conducted Kingside attack. There are also, however, examples of Queen sacrifices which allow a pawn to promote or which are a prelude to a win of enemy pieces in excess of the value of the Queen. In this last case it may be argued that it isn't really a sacrifice if more material is gained in return. Nonetheless, parting with the most powerful attacking piece in an unexpected manner is an esthetically pleasing conception.

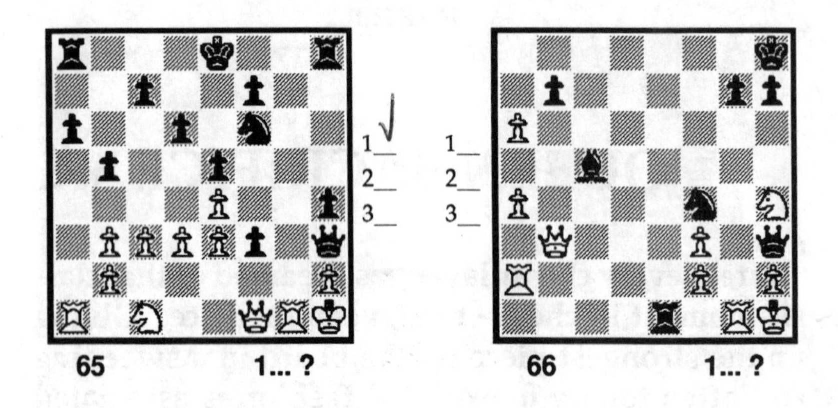
65 1... ?
66 1... ?

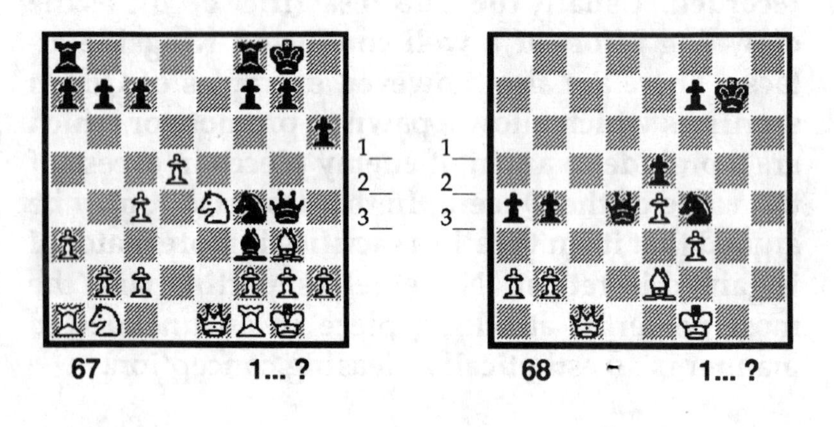
67 1... ?
68 1... ?

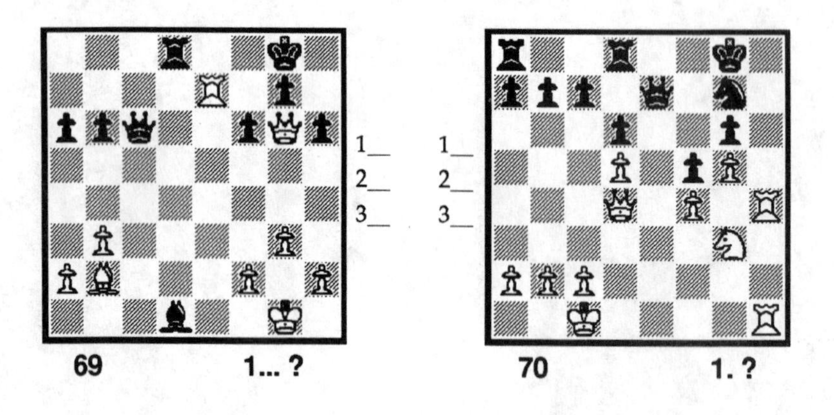
69 1... ?
70 1. ?

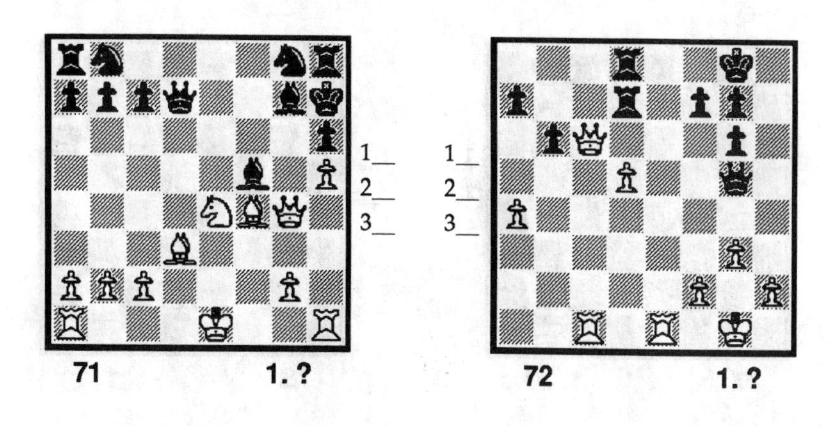
1__
2__
3__
1__
2__
3__
71
1. ?
72
1. ?

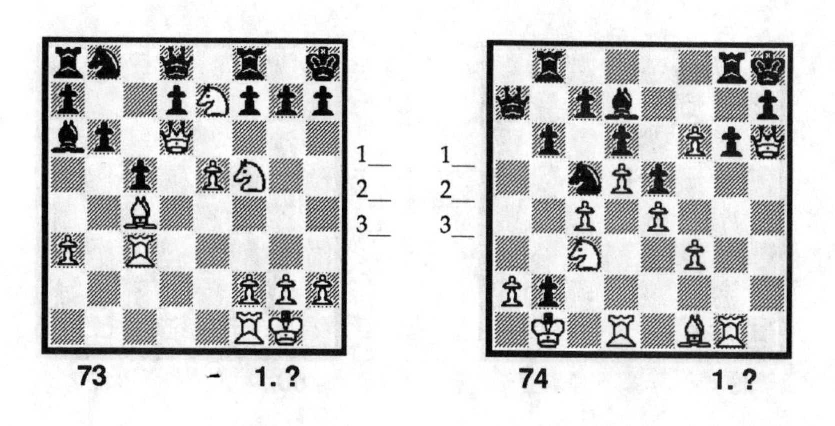
1__
2__
3__
1__
2__
3__
73
1. ?
74
1. ?

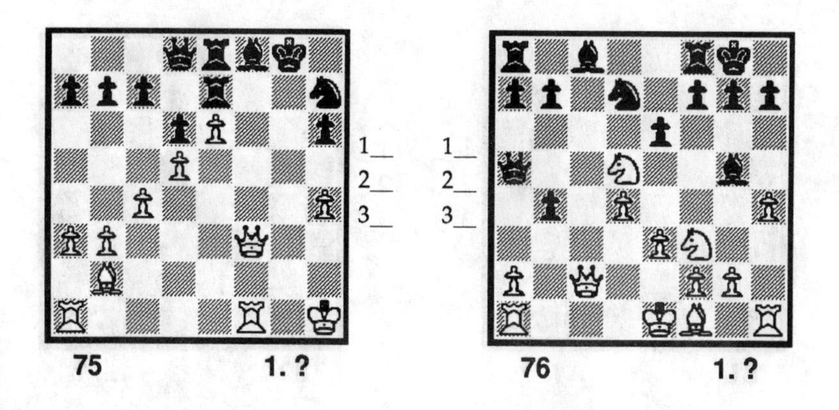
1__
2__
3__
1__
2__
3__
75
1. ?
76
1. ?

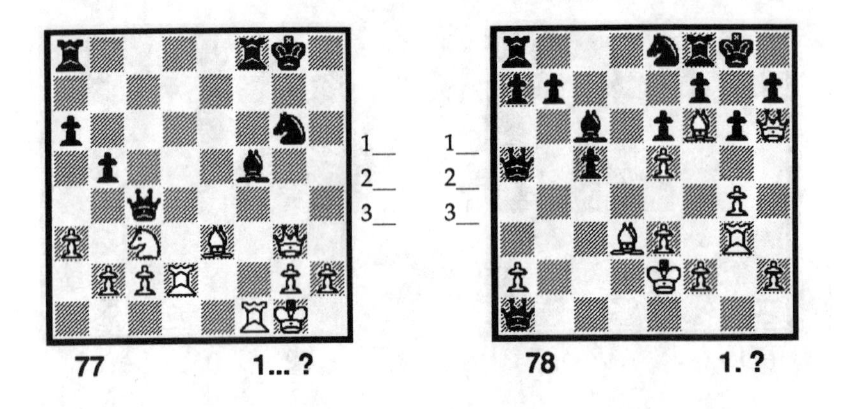

77 1... ?

78 1. ?

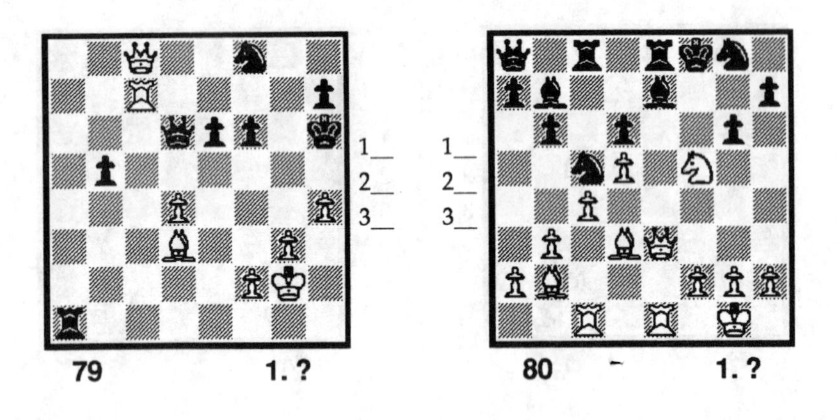

79 1. ?

80 1. ?

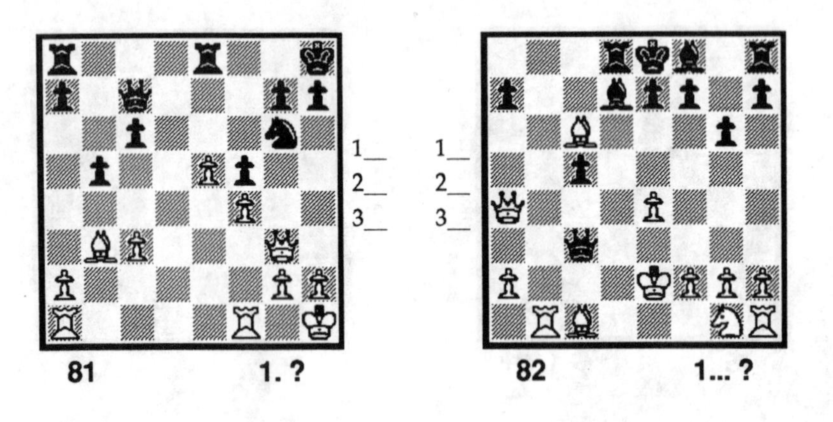

81 1. ?

82 1... ?

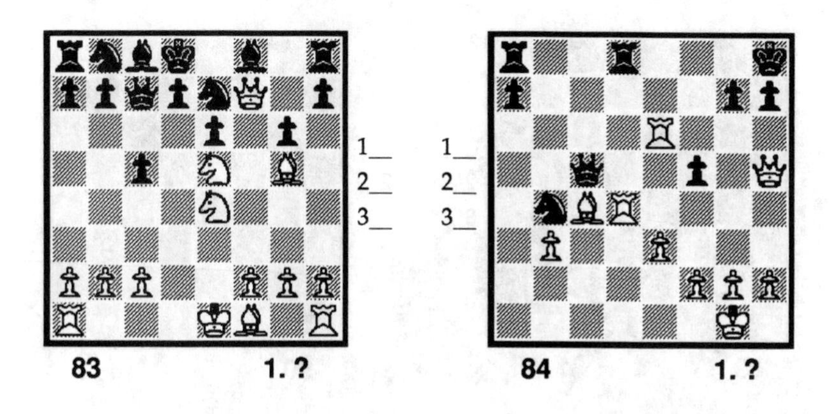
1__
2__
3__
1__
2__
3__
83
1. ?
84
1. ?

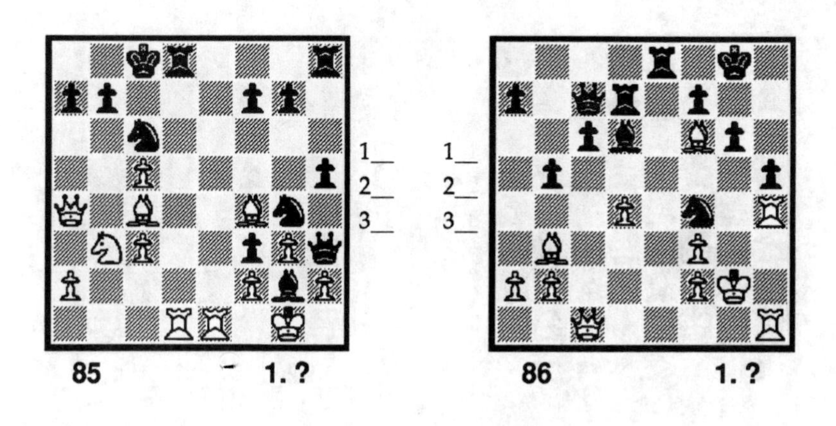
1__
2__
3__
1__
2__
3__
85
1. ?
86
1. ?

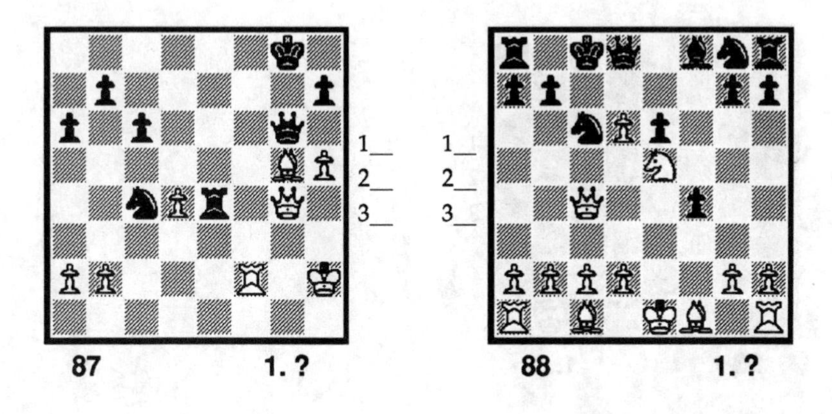
1__
2__
3__
1__
2__
3__
87
1. ?
88
1. ?

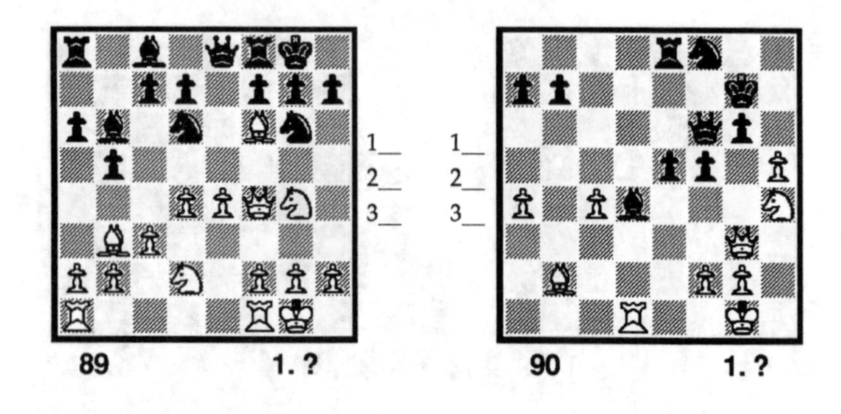

89 1. ?

1__
2__
3__

90 1. ?

1__
2__
3__

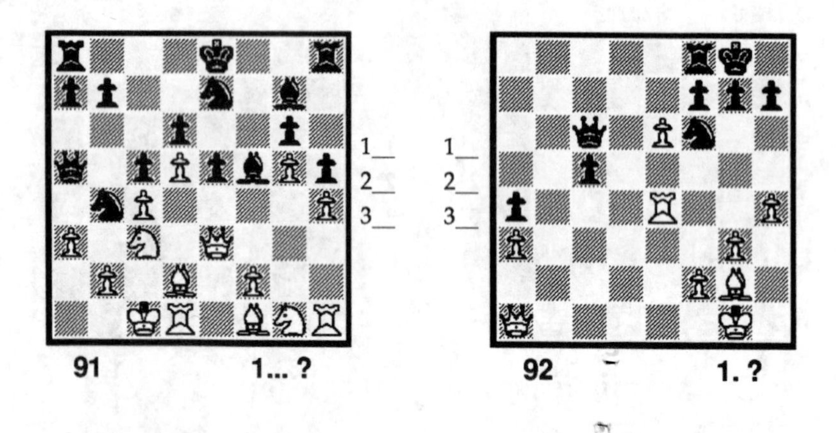

91 1... ?

1__
2__
3__

92 1. ?

1__
2__
3__

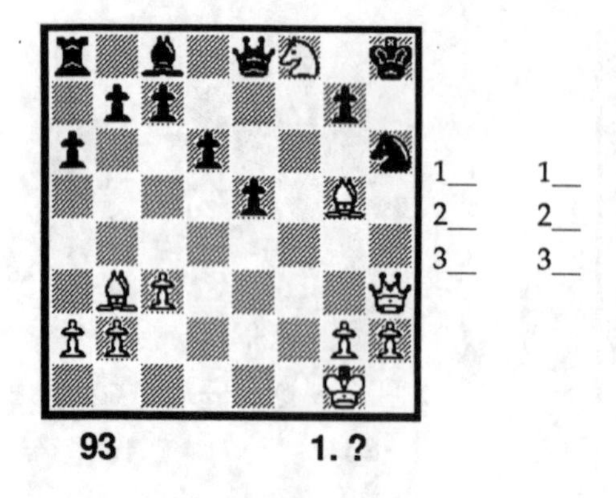

93 1. ?

1__
2__
3__

1__
2__
3__

CHAPTER 3

THE PIN

Pinning is one of the most frequently occurring tactical motifs. The pin involves an attack on an enemy piece which is situated on a straight line (i.e. a file, a rank, or a diagonal) and in front of a more valuable piece. Since the first attacked piece is less valuable, it dare not move because the more valuable piece behind it would be exposed to immediate attack. Hence the first piece "in line" is pinned down and, reluctantly, subject to capture.

There are two kinds of pins, the absolute and the relative pin. An absolute pin involves a piece in front of its King, which cannot legally move away to protect itself since this would leave the King in check. For this reason the absolute pin is normally very damaging. The relative pin is one without the King's involvement. In some of these cases the pinned piece may be able to move away if it can in turn produce a stronger threat of its own. For this reason relative pins must be examined with some degree of caution.

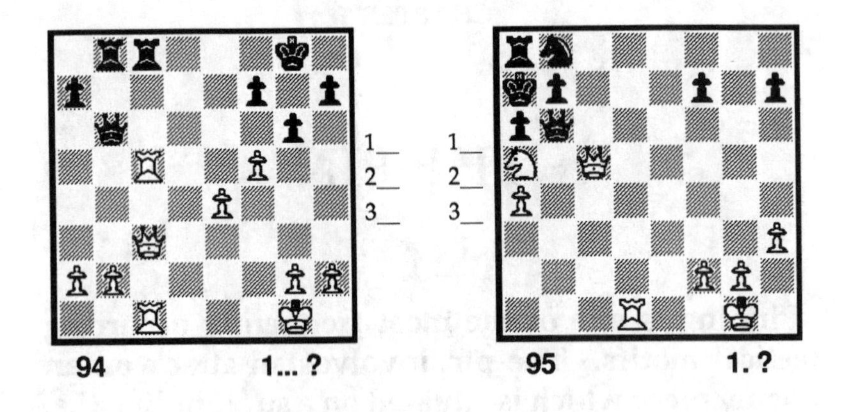

94 1... ?

95 1. ?

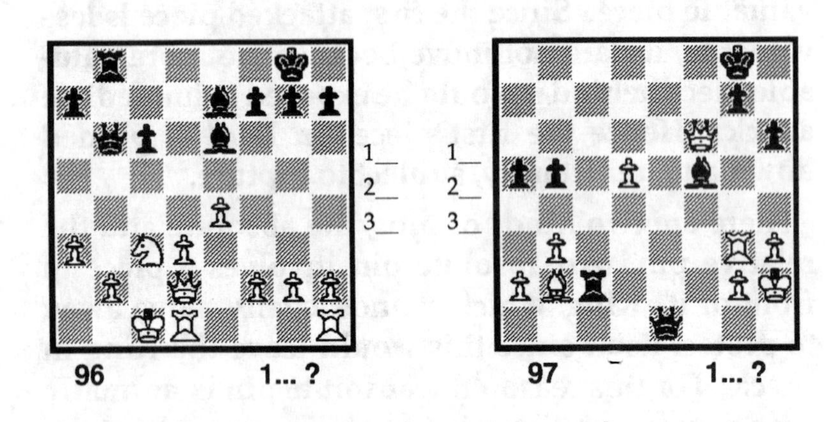

96 1... ?

97 1... ?

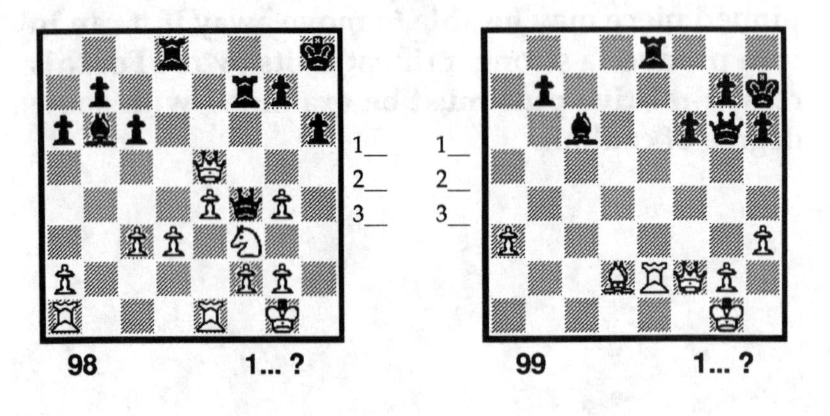

98 1... ?

99 1... ?

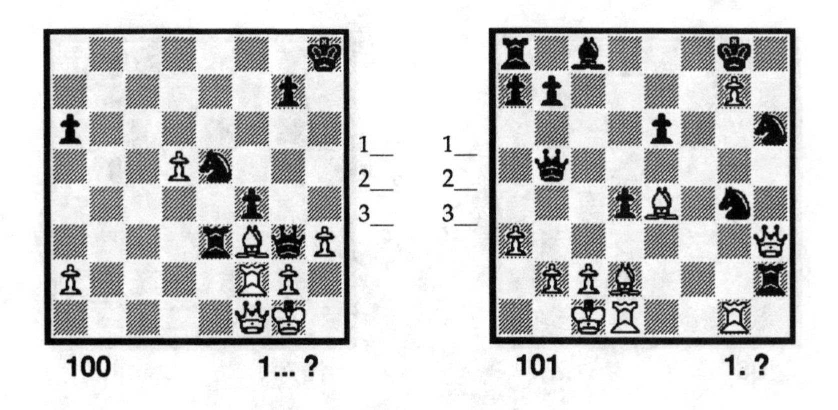
1__
2__
3__
1__
2__
3__
100
1... ?
101
1. ?

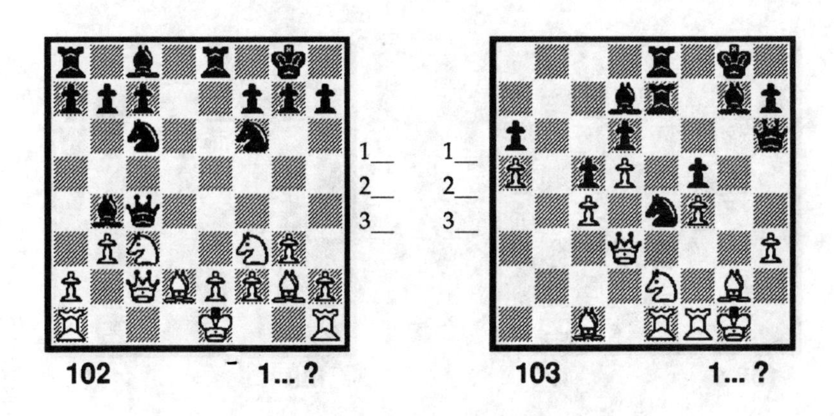
1__
2__
3__
1__
2__
3__
102
1... ?
103
1... ?

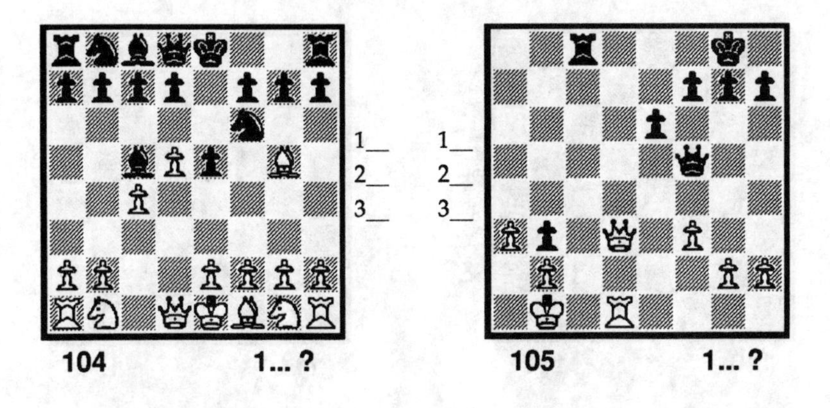
1__
2__
3__
1__
2__
3__
104
1... ?
105
1... ?

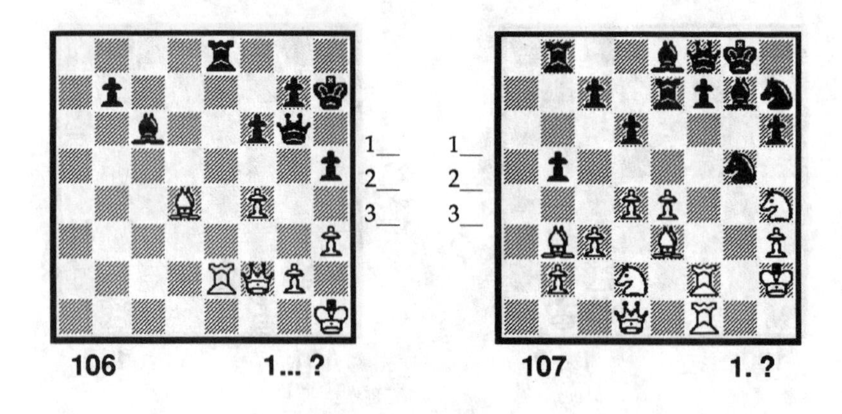
1__ 1__
2__ 2__
3__ 3__

106 1... ?

107 1. ?

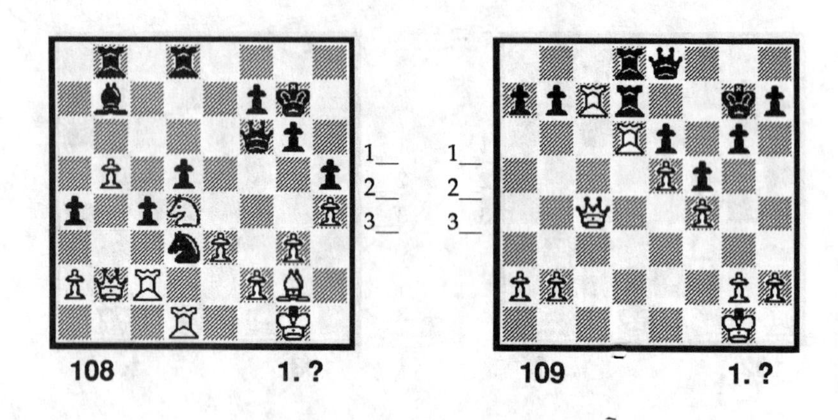
1__ 1__
2__ 2__
3__ 3__

108 1. ?

109 1. ?

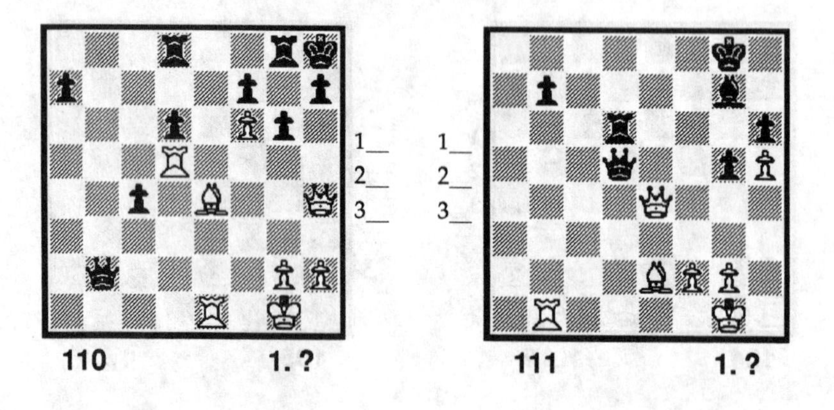
1__ 1__
2__ 2__
3__ 3__

110 1. ?

111 1. ?

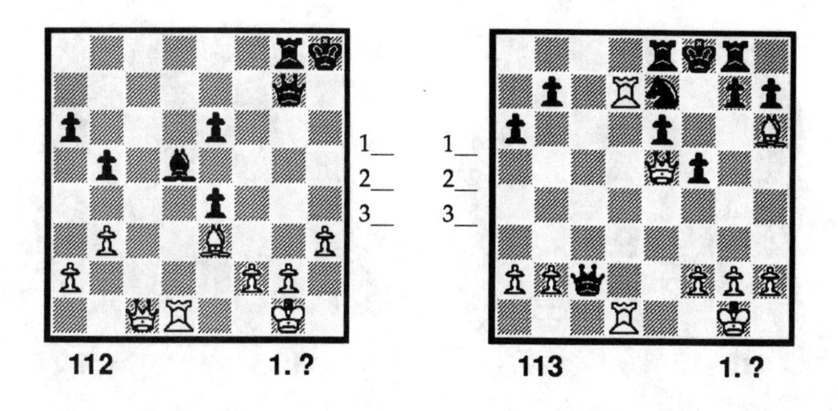

112 1. ?

113 1. ?

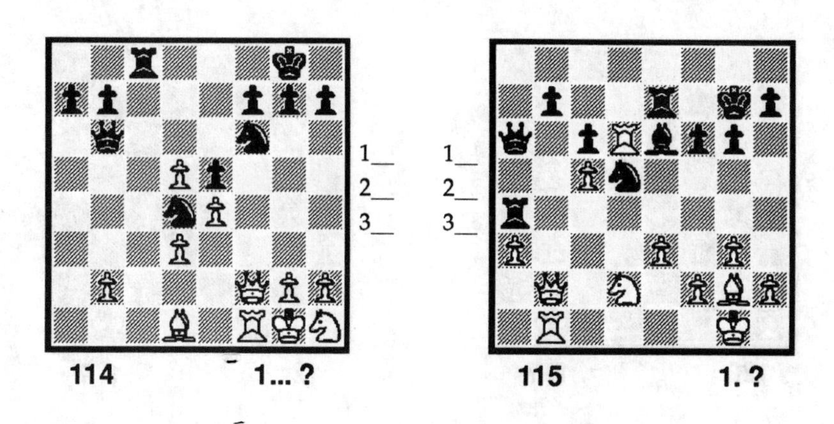

114 1... ?

115 1. ?

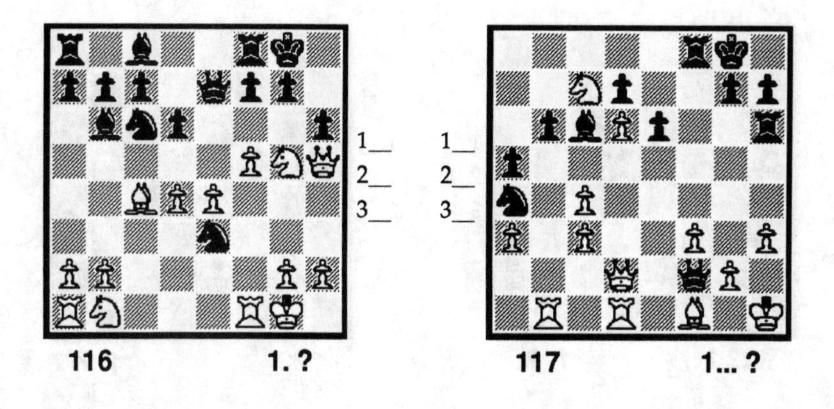

116 1. ?

117 1... ?

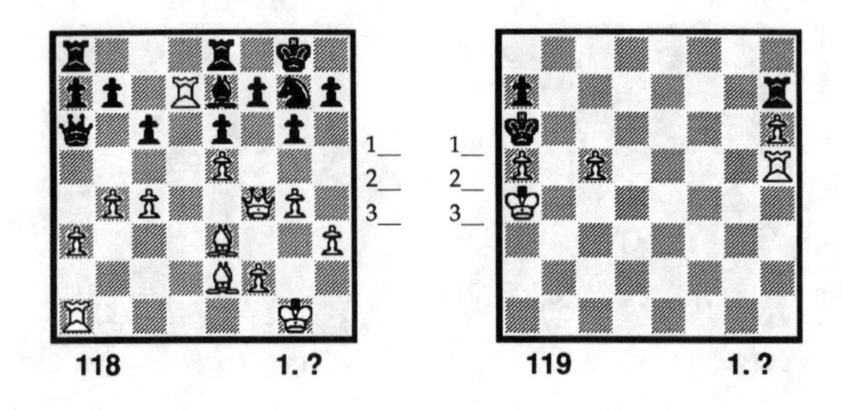
1__
2__
3__
1__
2__
3__
118
1. ?
119
1. ?

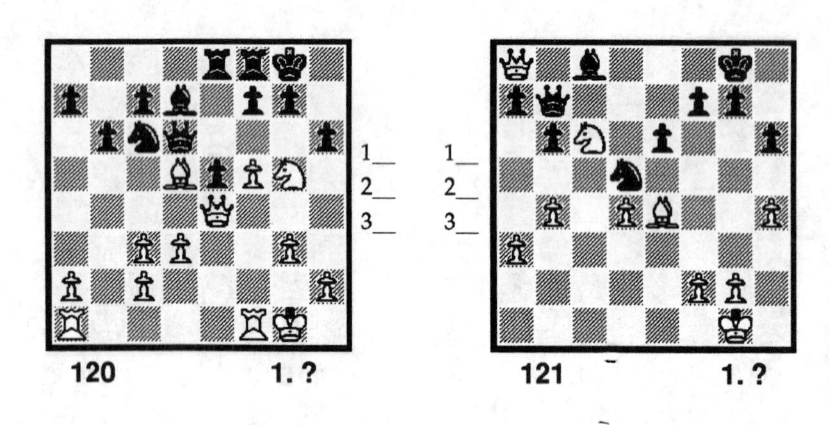
1__
2__
3__
1__
2__
3__
120
1. ?
121
1. ?

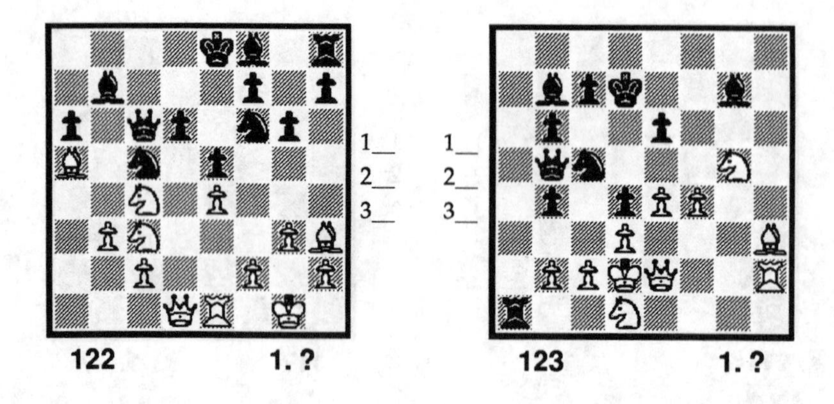
1__
2__
3__
1__
2__
3__
122
1. ?
123
1. ?

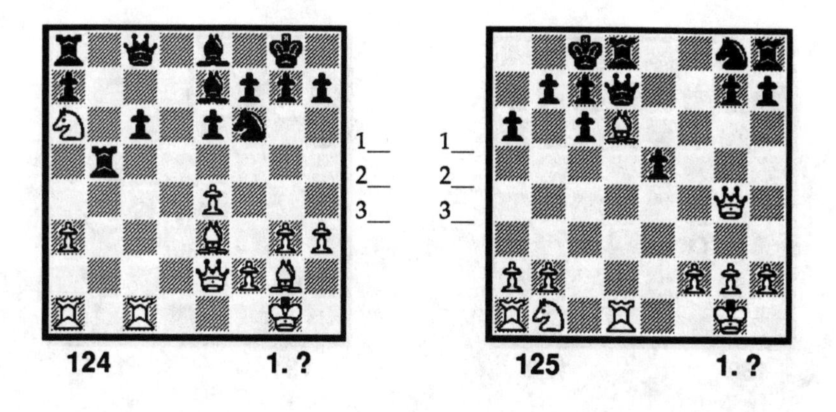

124 1. ?

125 1. ?

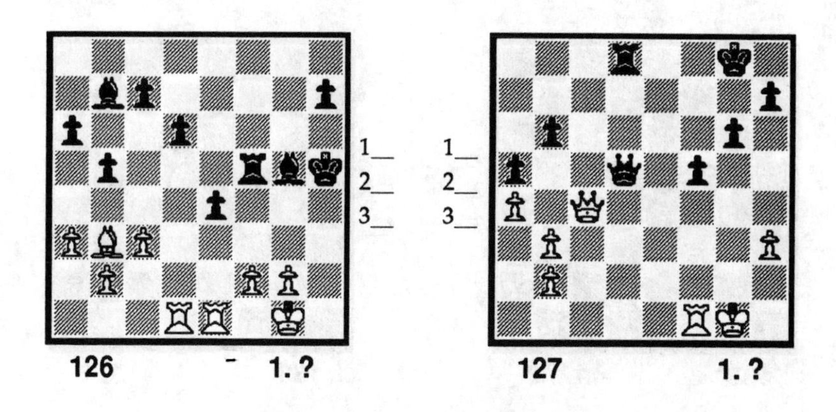

126 1. ?

127 1. ?

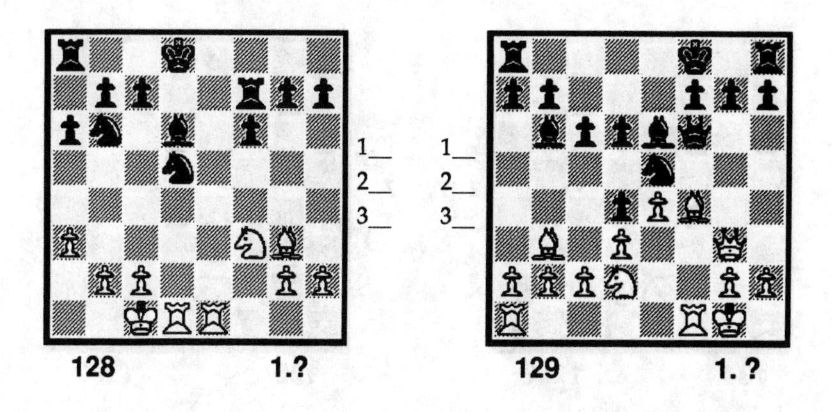

128 1.?

129 1. ?

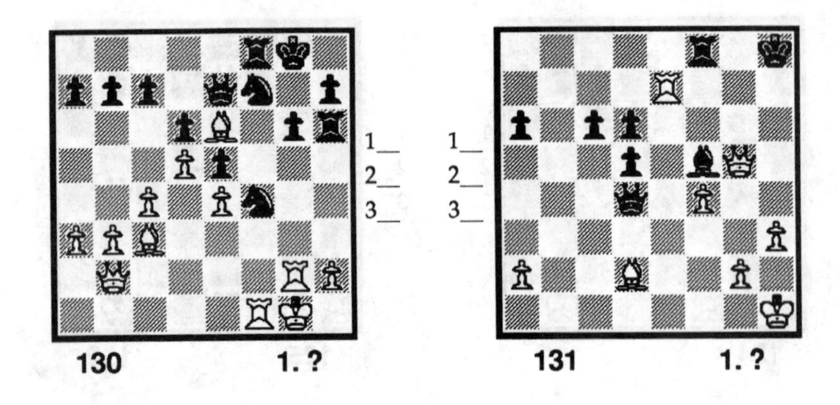

130 1. ?

131 1. ?

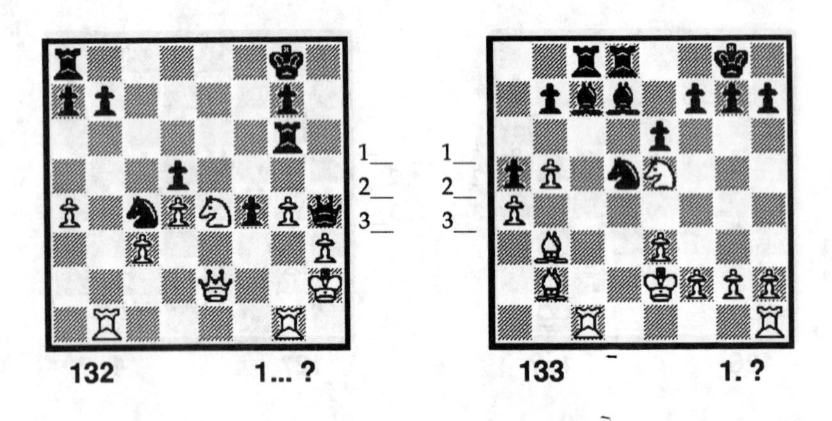

132 1... ?

133 1. ?

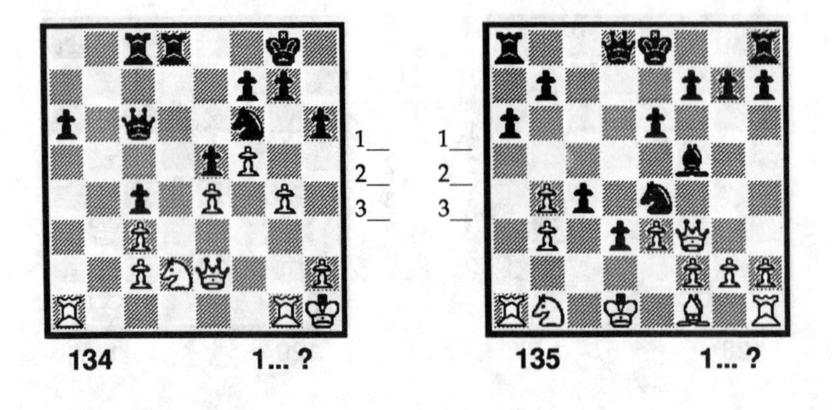

134 1... ?

135 1... ?

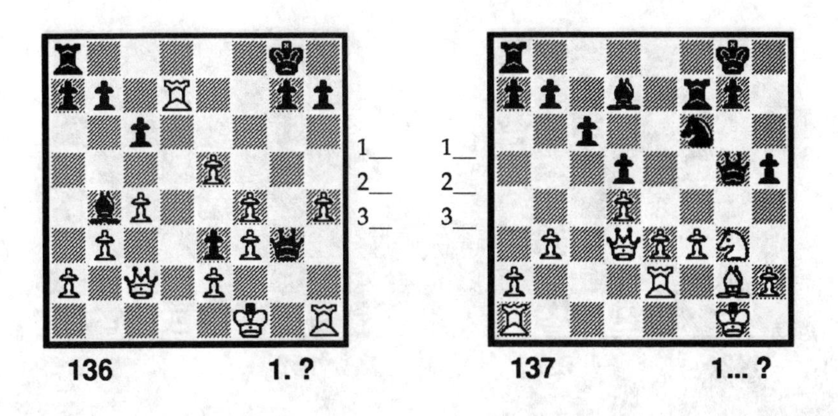

1__ 1__
2__ 2__
3__ 3__

136 1. ?

137 1... ?

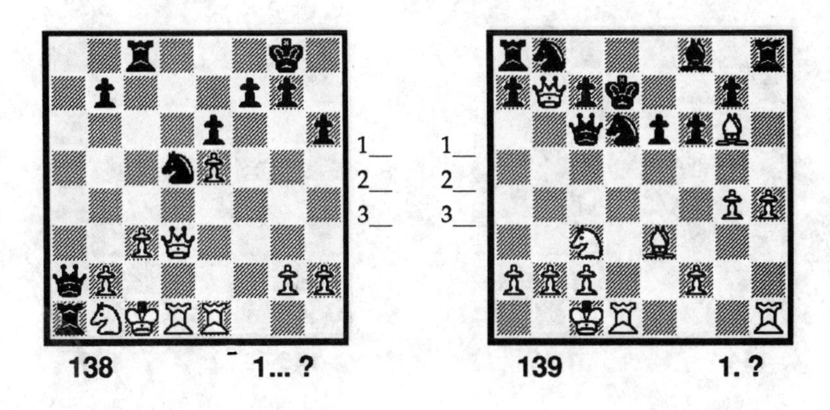

1__ 1__
2__ 2__
3__ 3__

138 1... ?

139 1. ?

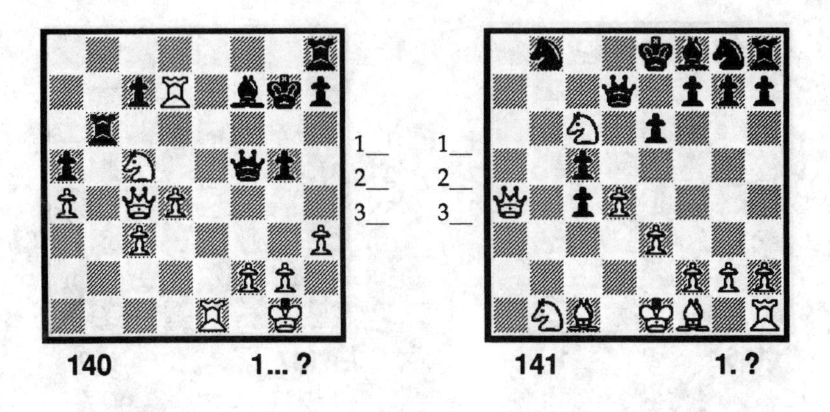

1__ 1__
2__ 2__
3__ 3__

140 1... ?

141 1. ?

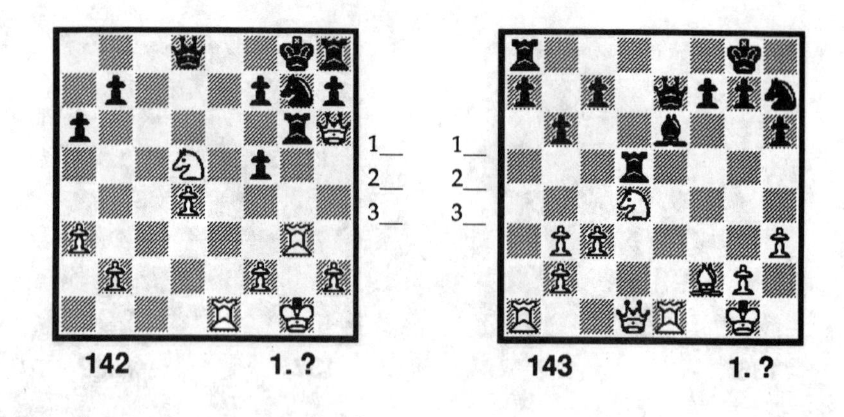
1__
2__
3__
1__
2__
3__
142
1. ?
143
1. ?

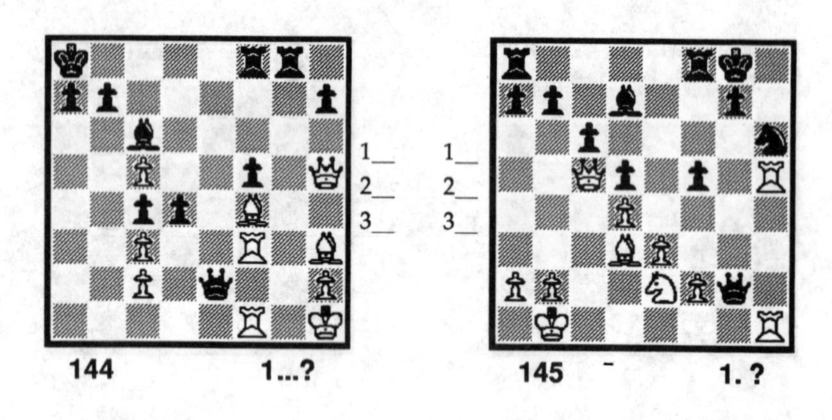
1__
2__
3__
1__
2__
3__
144
1...?
145
1. ?

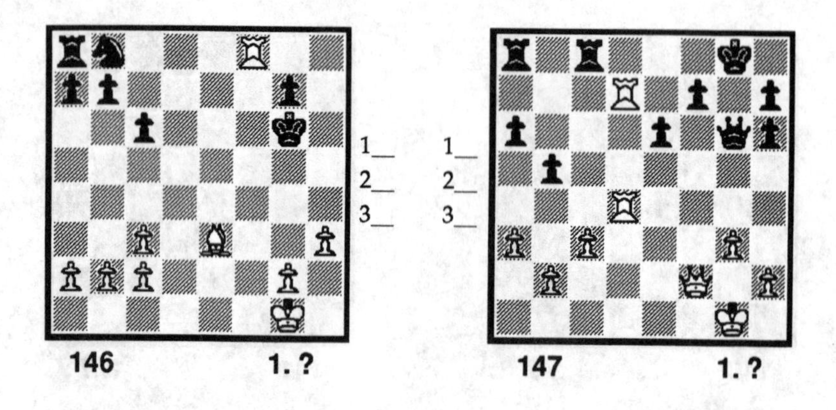
1__
2__
3__
1__
2__
3__
146
1. ?
147
1. ?

CHAPTER 4

KNIGHT FORK

The Knight is the most fascinating and mysterious of all the chess pieces. Its singular ability to hop over all obstacles, both friend and foe, set it apart. Potentially the Knight can attack up to eight pieces at once. In reality it is rare to encounter a Knight fork against more than two enemy units. The Knight fork is quite often prepared by a preliminary sacrifice or diversionary move. In any event, the Knight is very often the source of intriguing tactical play as it leaps unexpectedly into the thick of things.

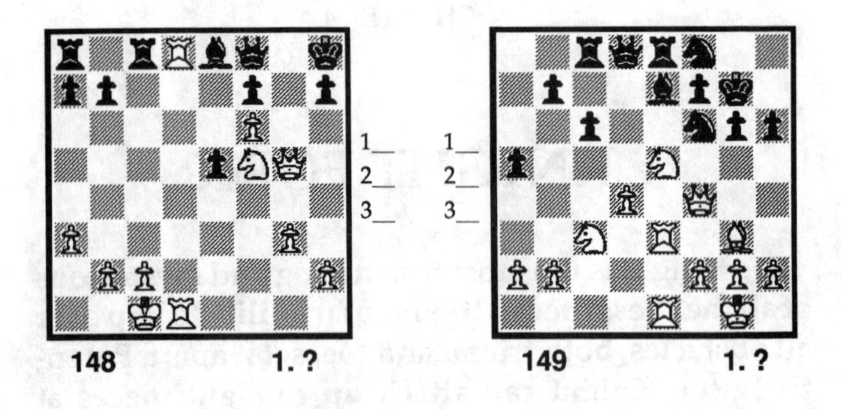

148 1. ?

149 1. ?

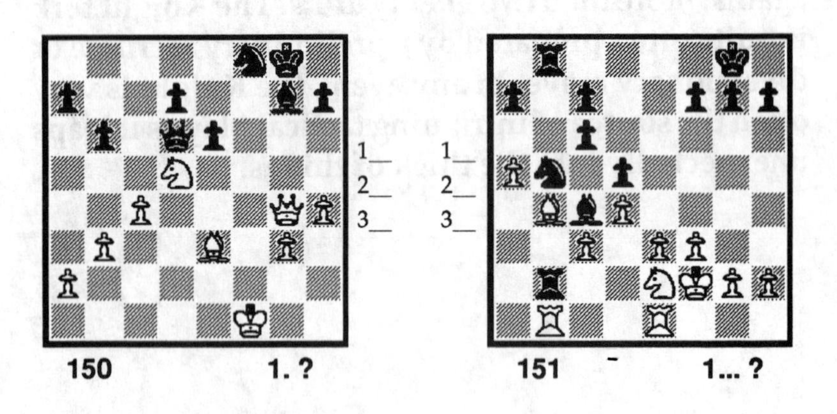

150 1. ?

151 1... ?

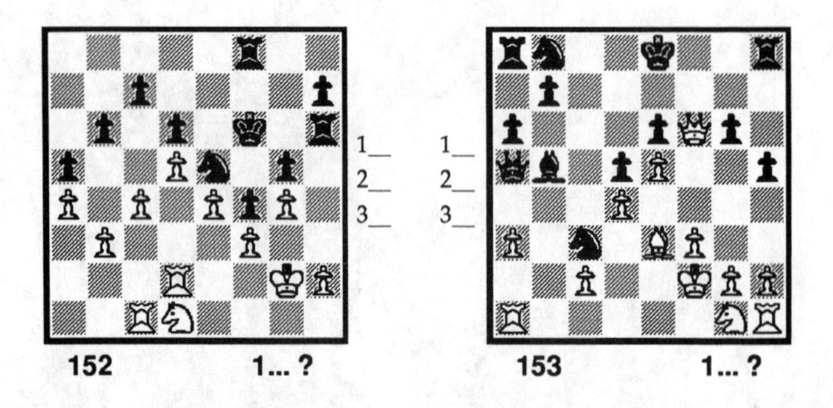

152 1... ?

153 1... ?

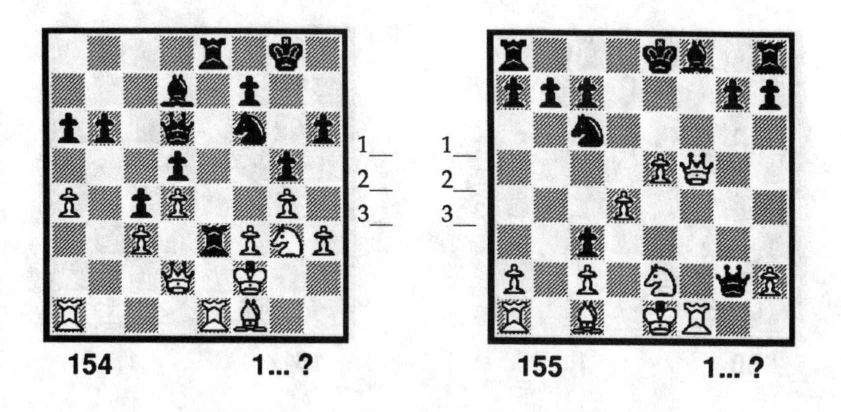

154 1... ?

155 1... ?

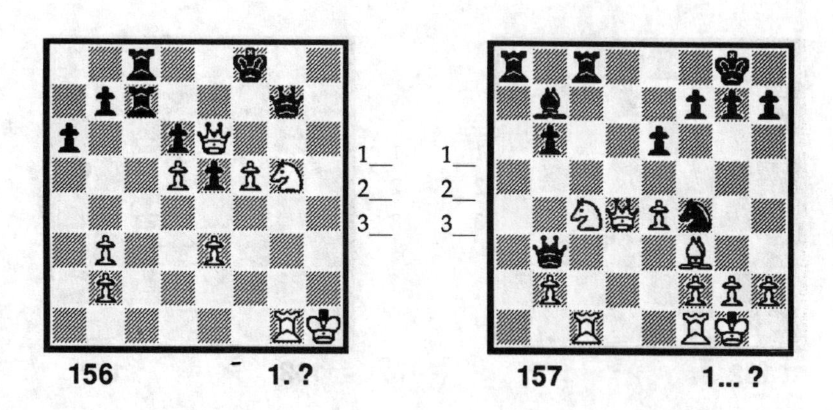

156 1. ?

157 1... ?

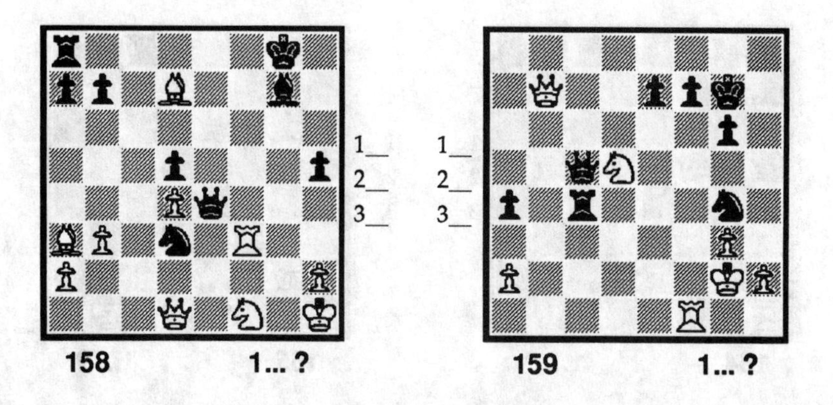

158 1... ?

159 1... ?

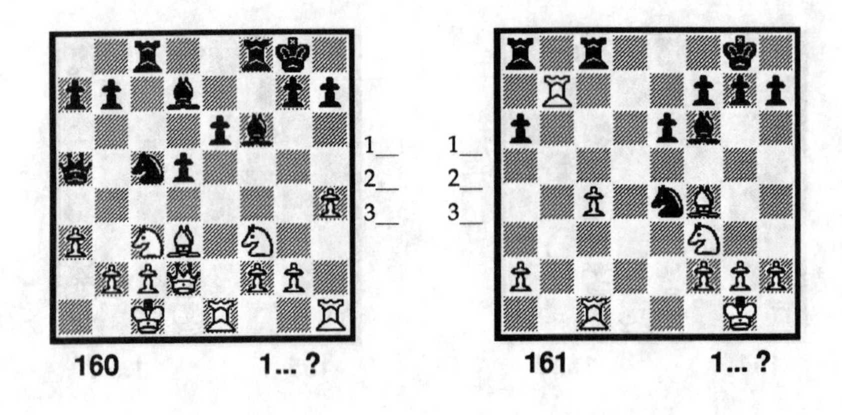

160 1... ?

161 1... ?

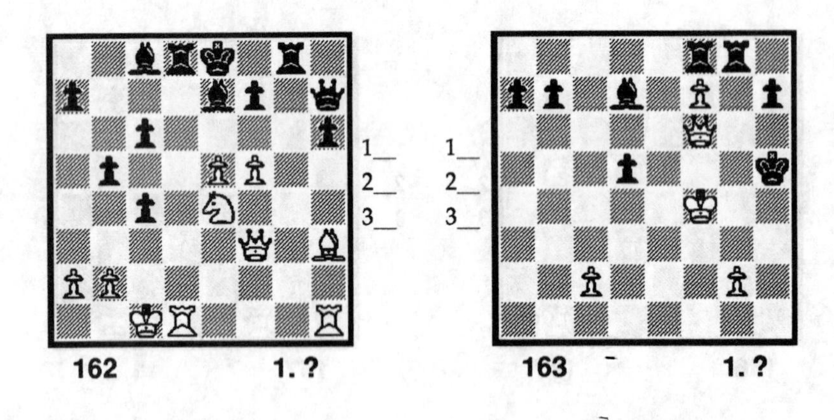

162 1. ?

163 1. ?

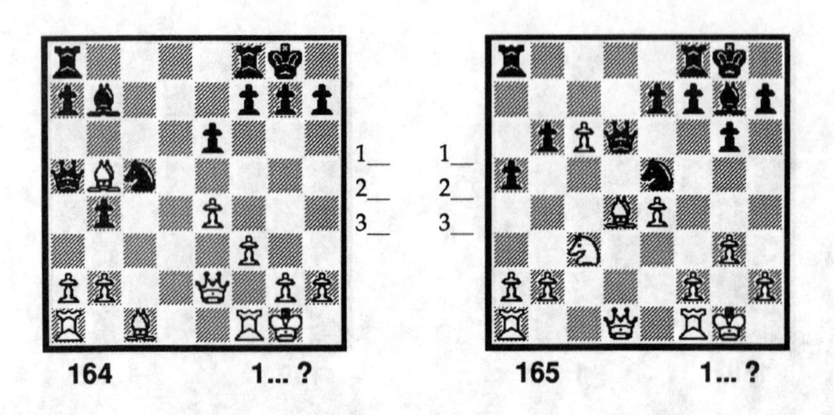

164 1... ?

165 1... ?

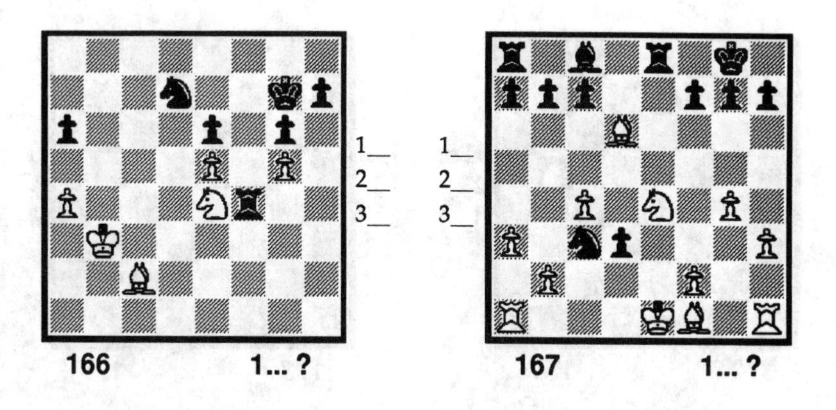

166 1... ? 167 1... ?

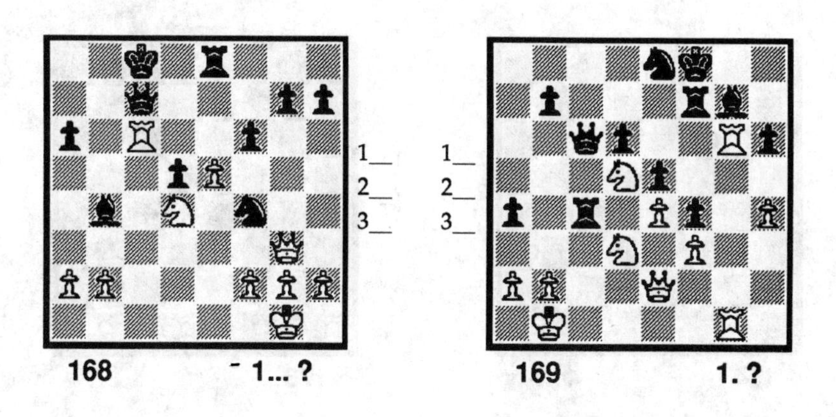

168 1... ? 169 1. ?

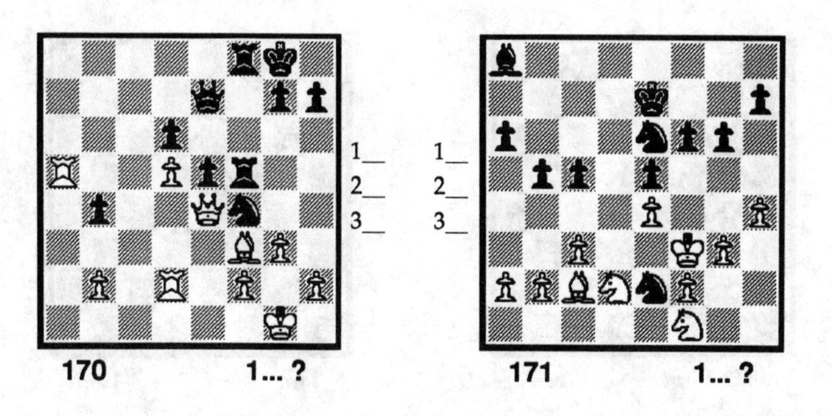

170 1... ? 171 1... ?

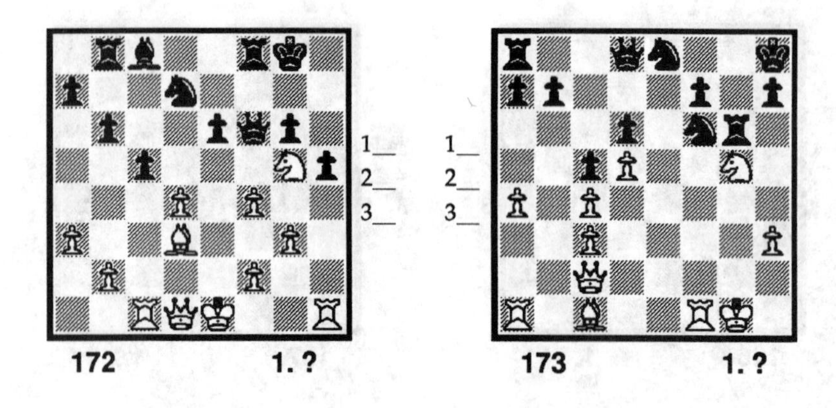
172
1. ?
1__
2__
3__
1__
2__
3__
173
1. ?

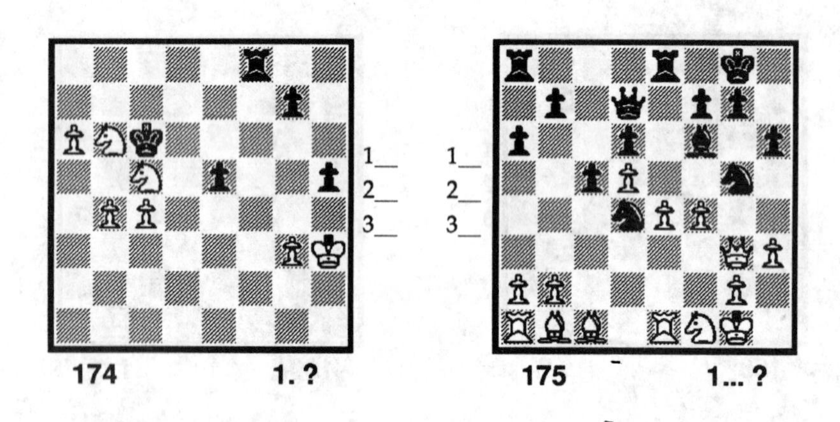
174
1. ?
1__
2__
3__
1__
2__
3__
175
1... ?

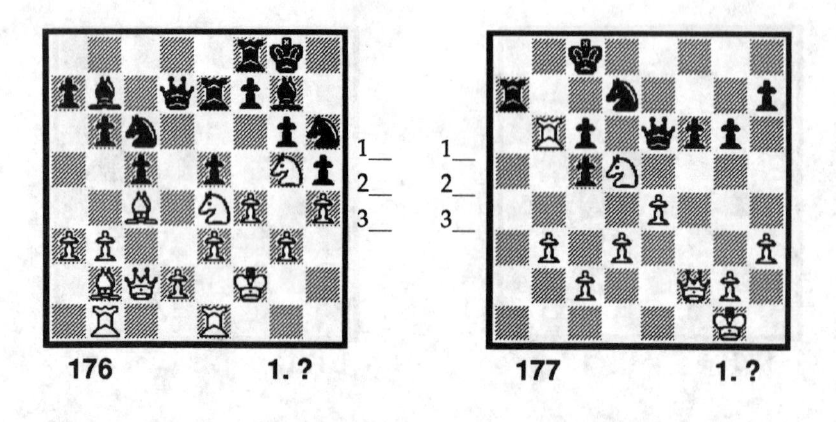
176
1. ?
1__
2__
3__
1__
2__
3__
177
1. ?

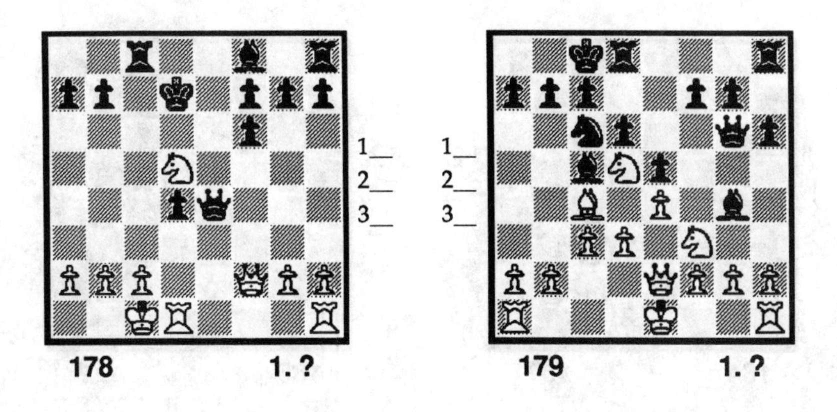

178 1. ?

179 1. ?

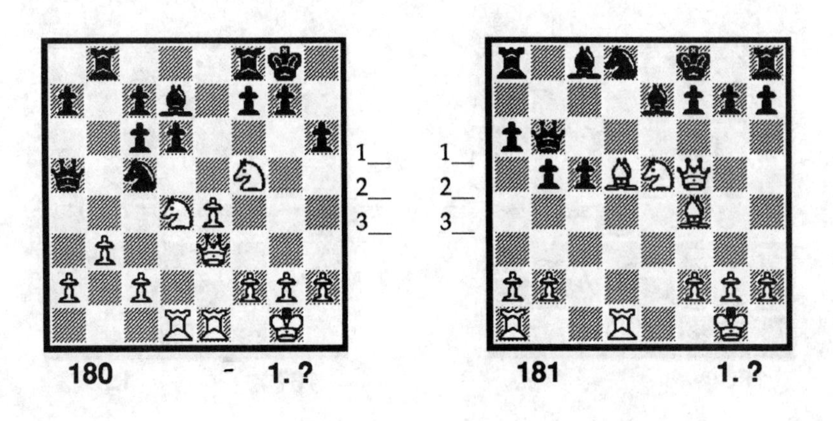

180 1. ?

181 1. ?

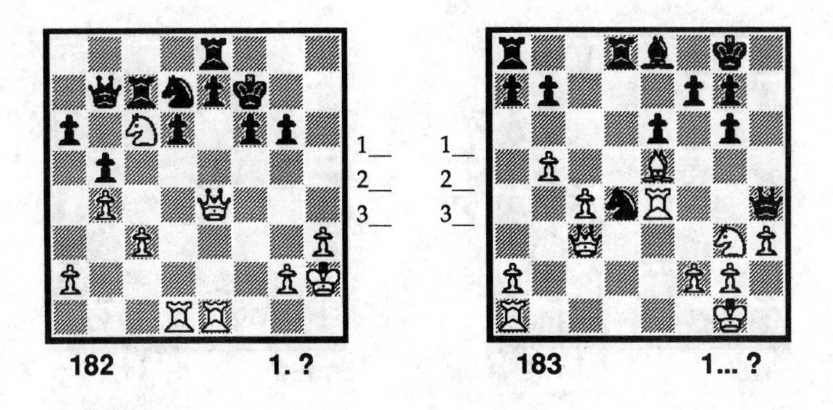

182 1. ?

183 1... ?

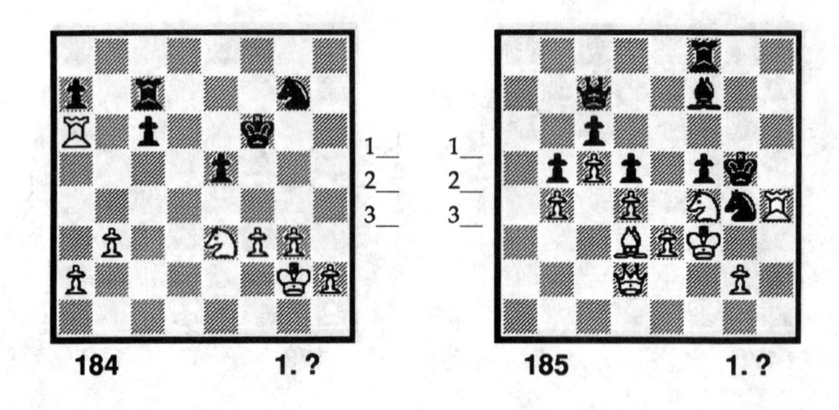

184 1. ?

185 1. ?

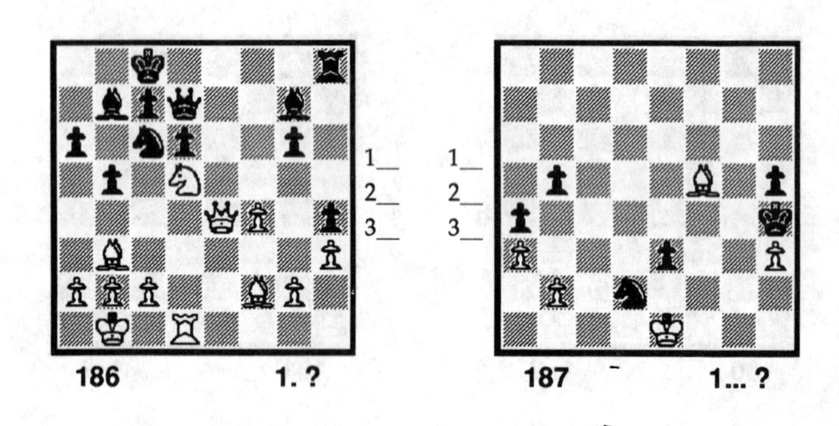

186 1. ?

187 1... ?

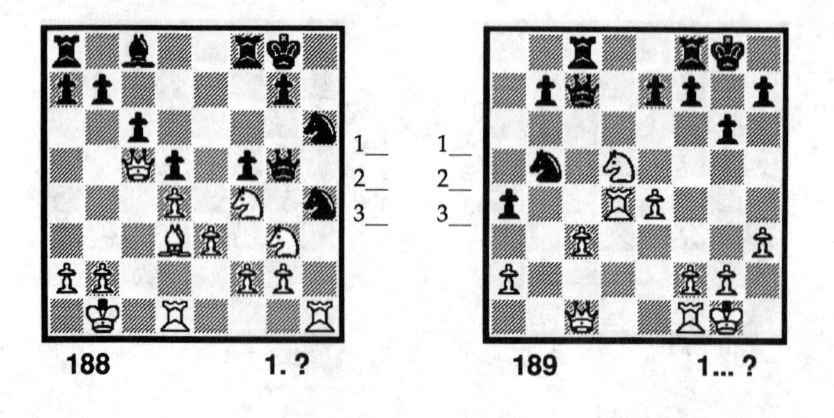

188 1. ?

189 1... ?

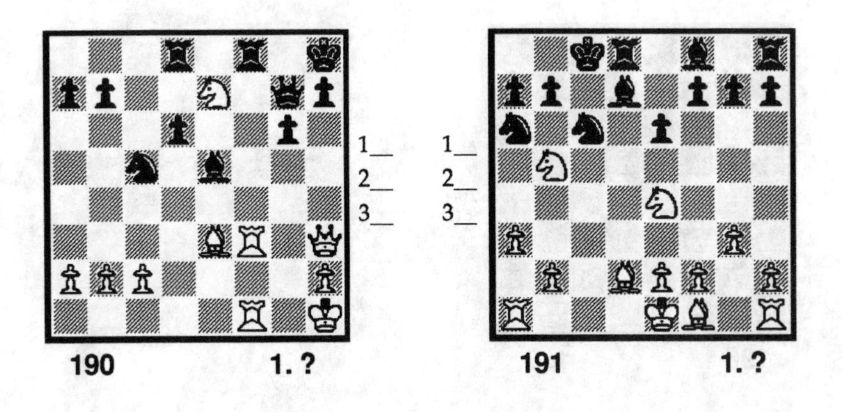

190 1. ?

191 1. ?

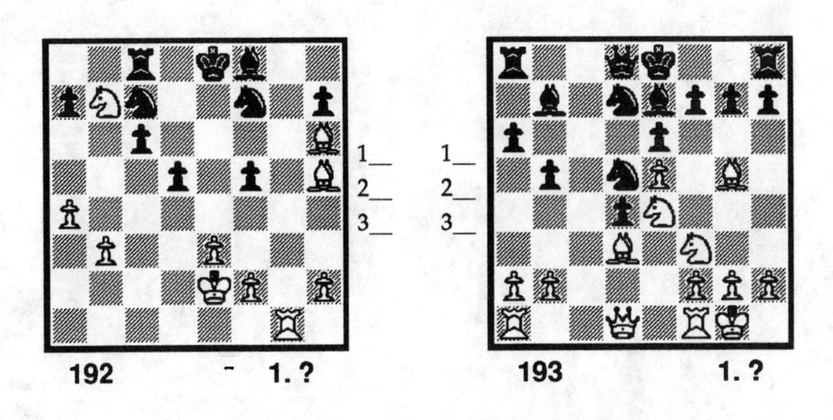

192 1. ?

193 1. ?

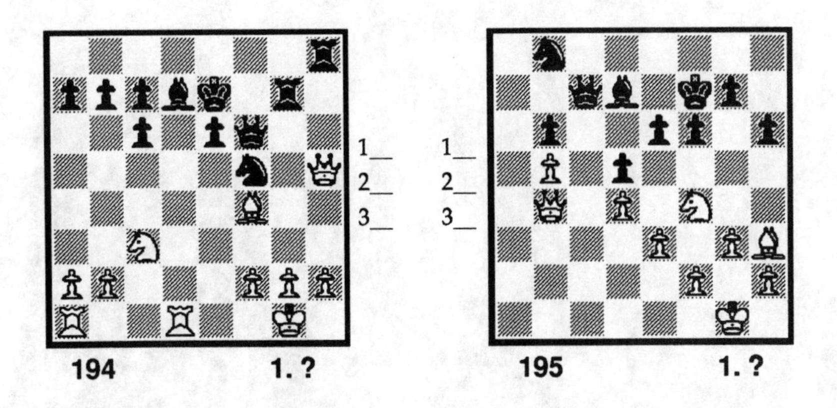

194 1. ?

195 1. ?

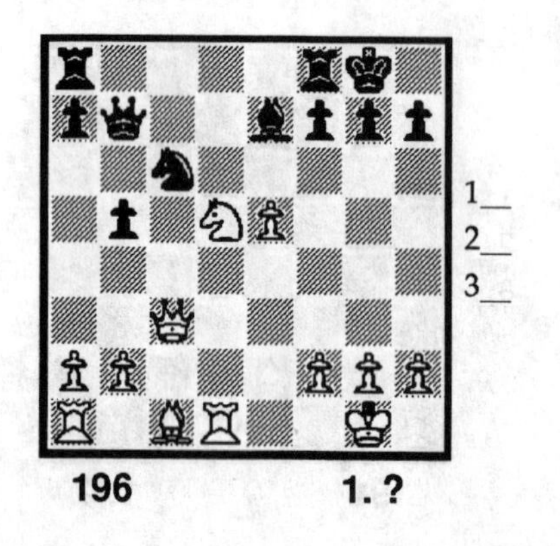

196 1. ?

CHAPTER 5

DOUBLE ATTACK

As the name implies, the double attack is a simultaneous attack on two enemy pieces. It should be noted that the Knight fork is a particularly infamous form of the double attack. Due to the intrinsic peculiarity of the Knight's move (it is the only piece which can "jump" over other pieces) and its fascinating symbolic impression-largely from its association with medieval horsemen-it has become traditional to consider the Knight fork as a separate tactical motif. Every piece can potentially double attack enemy units, even the lowly pawn is often involved. Very impressive is the long range striking power of the Queen in double attack situations, although the Rook and (more rarely) the Bishop can offer fine examples.

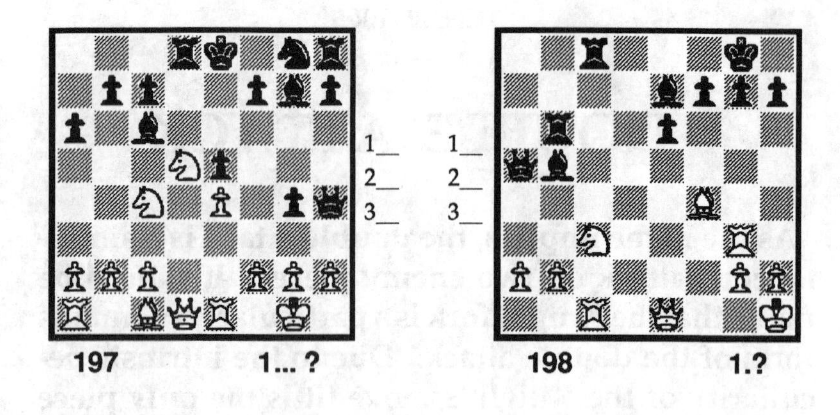
197 1... ?

198 1.?

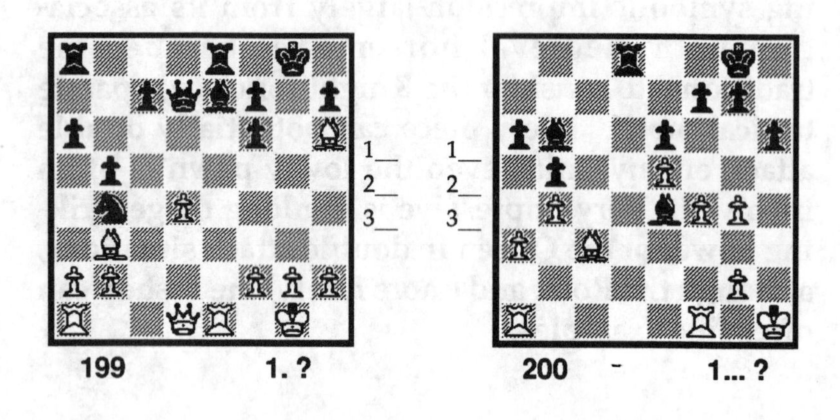
199 1. ?

200 1... ?

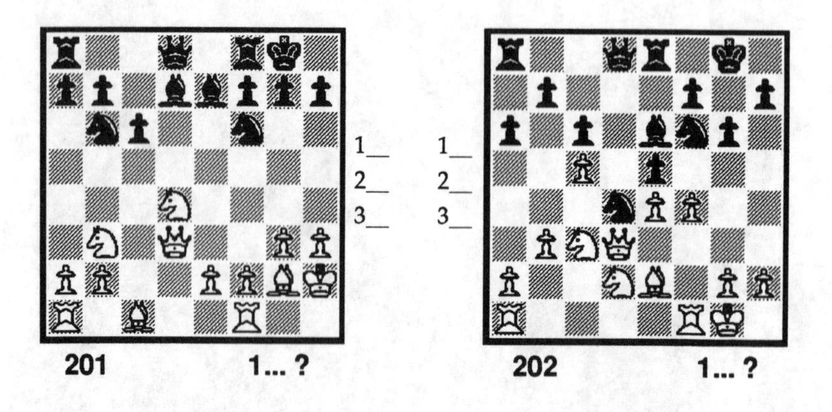
201 1... ?

202 1... ?

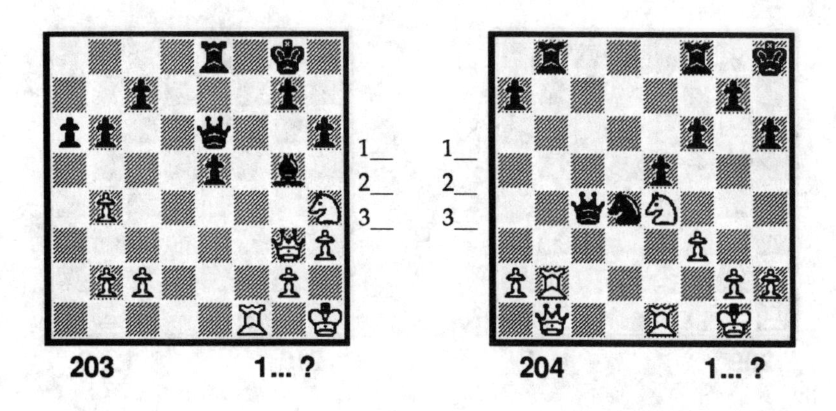
1__
2__
3__
1__
2__
3__
203
1... ?
204
1... ?

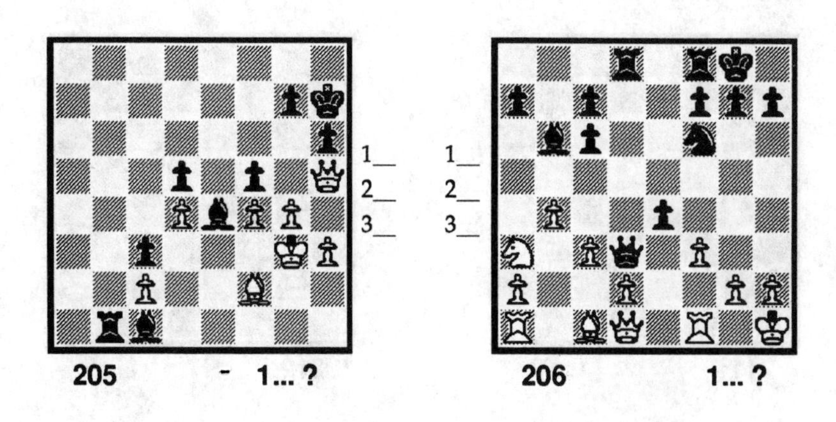
1__
2__
3__
1__
2__
3__
205
1... ?
206
1... ?

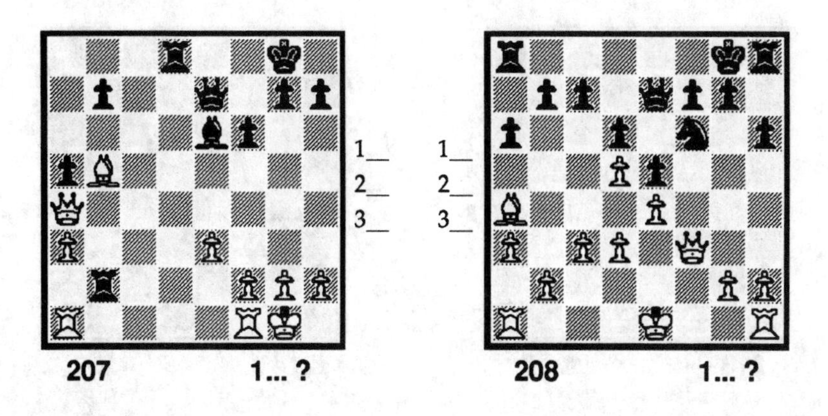
1__
2__
3__
1__
2__
3__
207
1... ?
208
1... ?

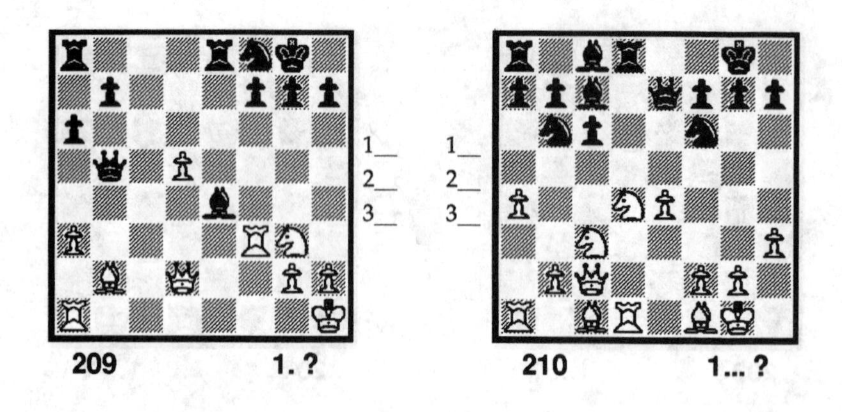
1__
2__
3__
1__
2__
3__
209 1. ?
210 1... ?

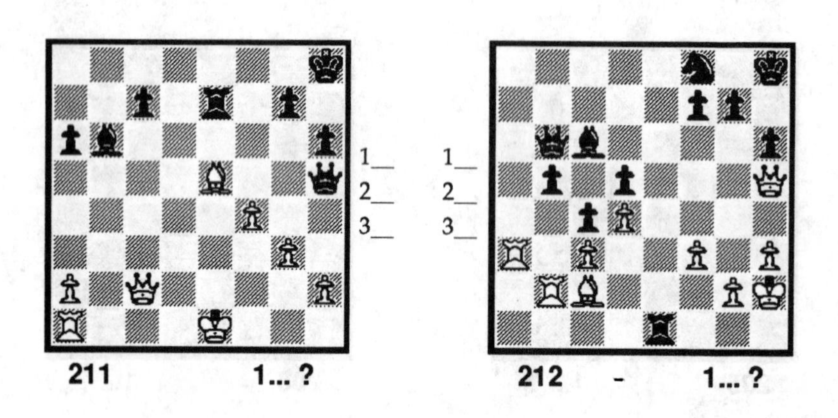
1__
2__
3__
1__
2__
3__
211 1... ?
212 - 1... ?

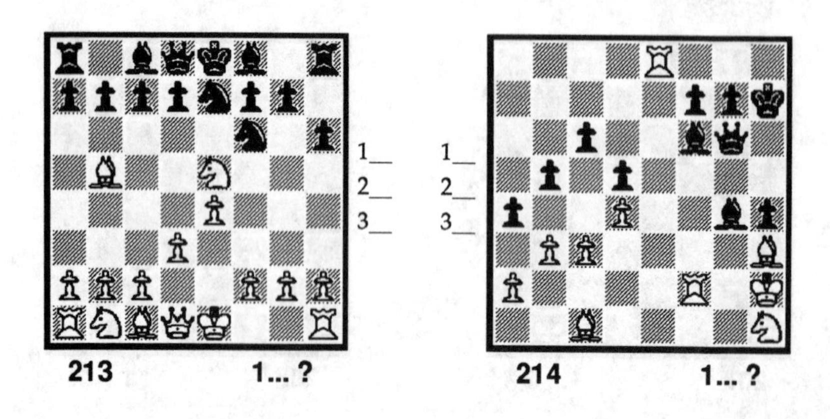
1__
2__
3__
1__
2__
3__
213 1... ?
214 1... ?

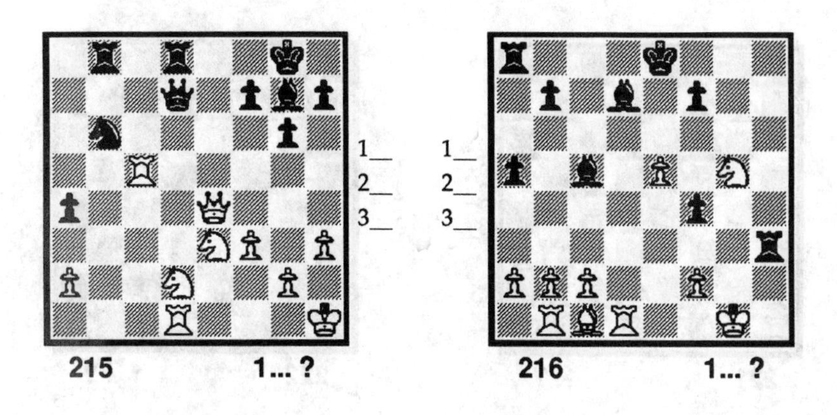

215 1... ?

216 1... ?

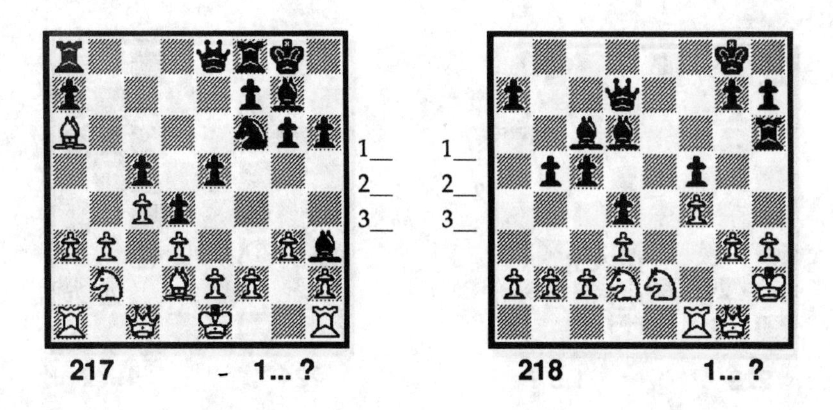

217 1... ?

218 1... ?

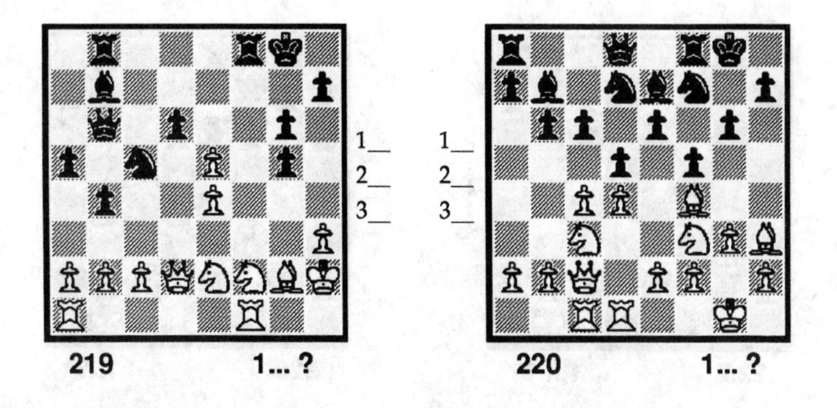

219 1... ?

220 1... ?

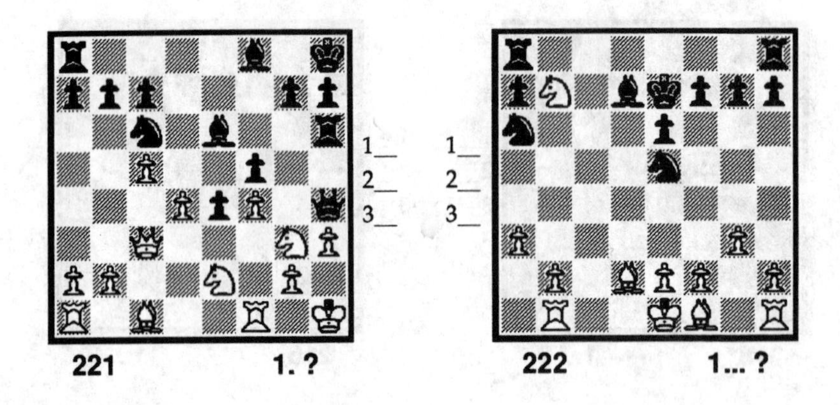
221 1. ? 222 1... ?

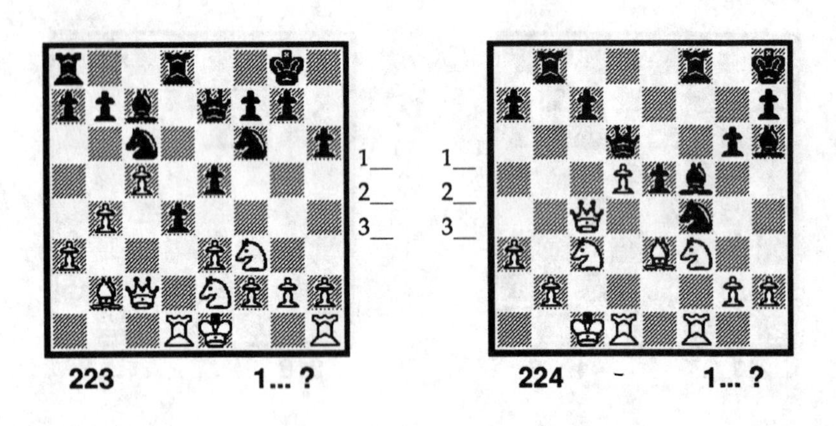
223 1... ? 224 1... ?

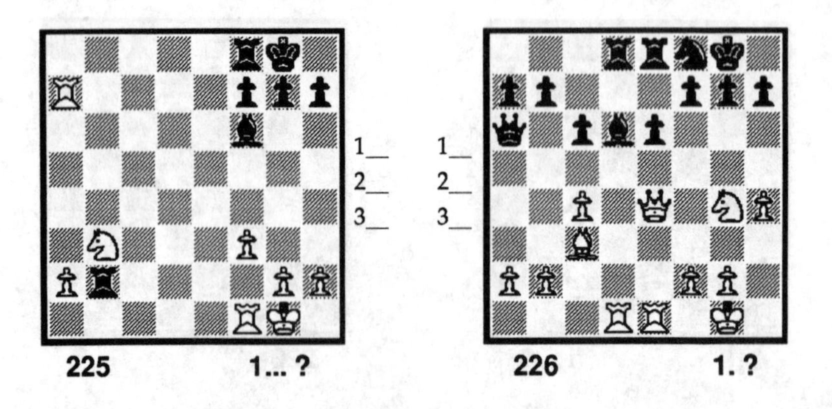
225 1... ? 226 1. ?

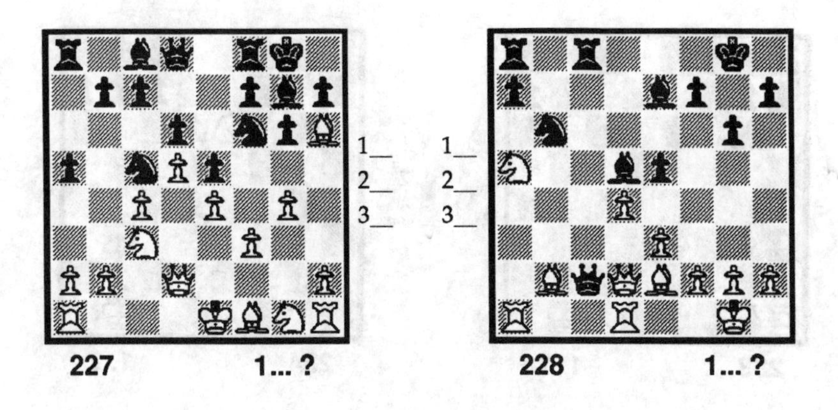

227 1... ?

228 1... ?

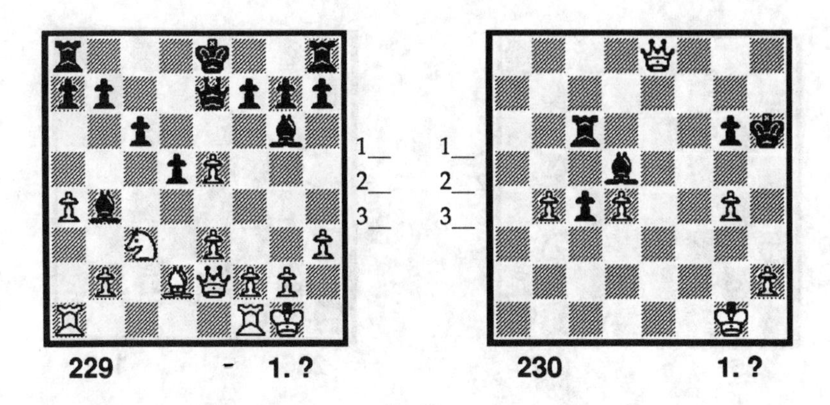

229 1. ?

230 1. ?

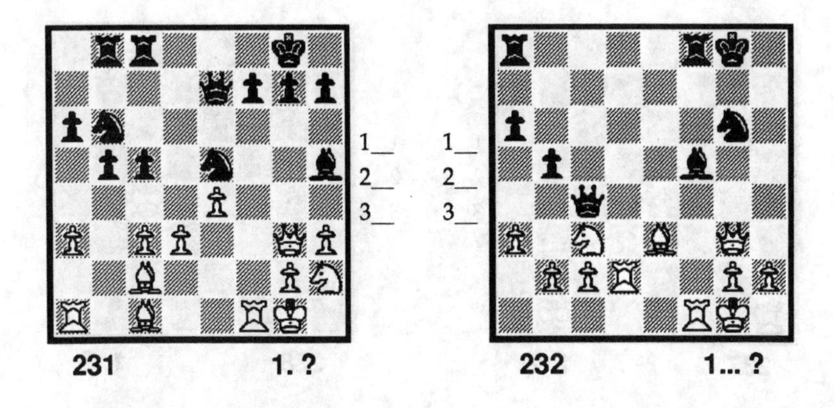

231 1. ?

232 1... ?

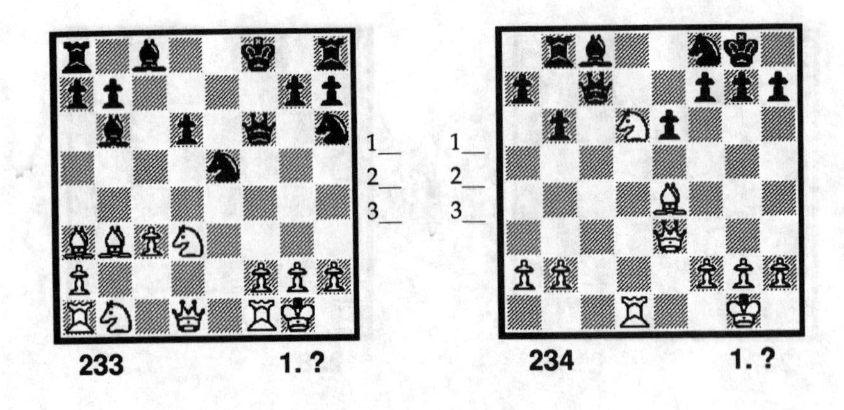

233 1. ?

234 1. ?

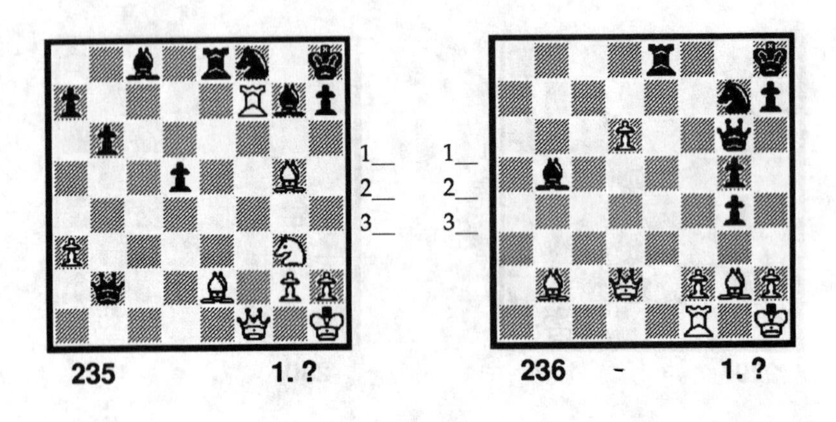

235 1. ?

236 1. ?

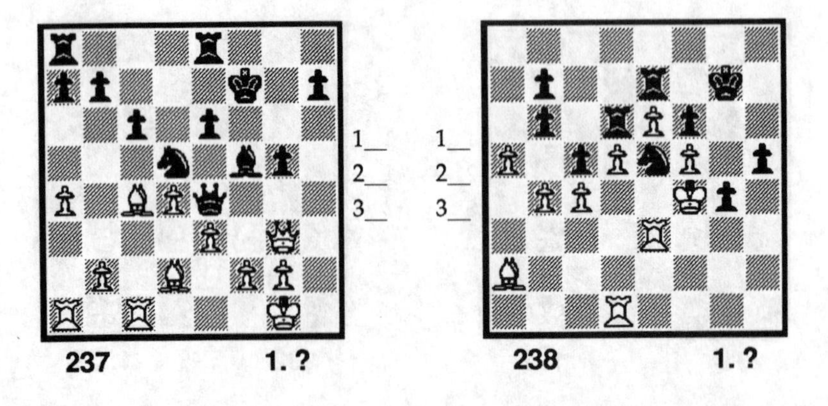

237 1. ?

238 1. ?

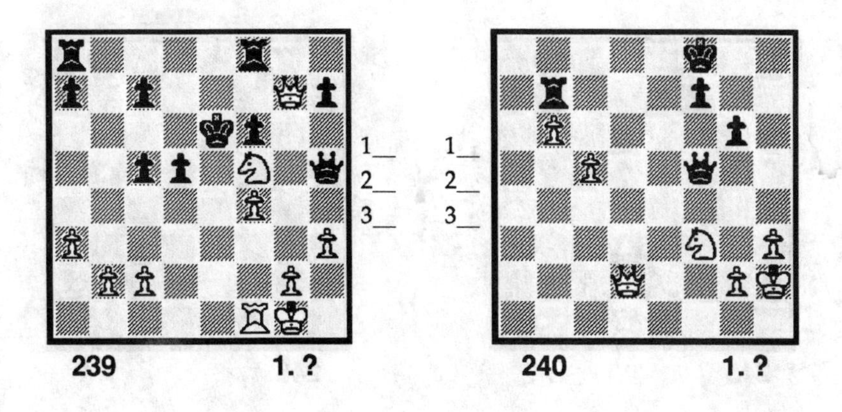

239 1. ? 240 1. ?

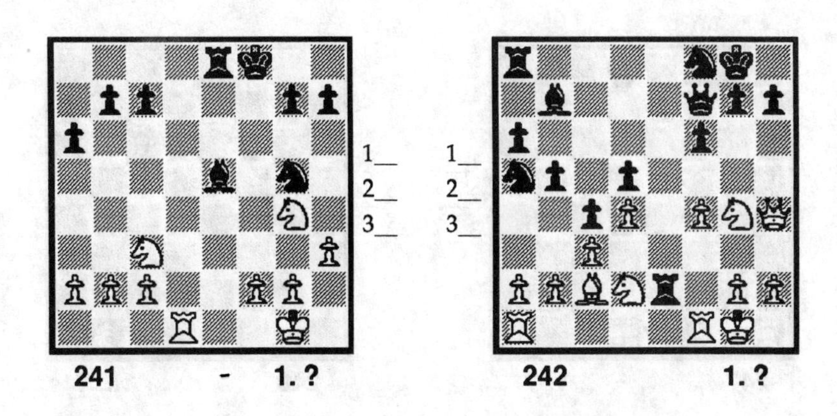

241 1. ? 242 1. ?

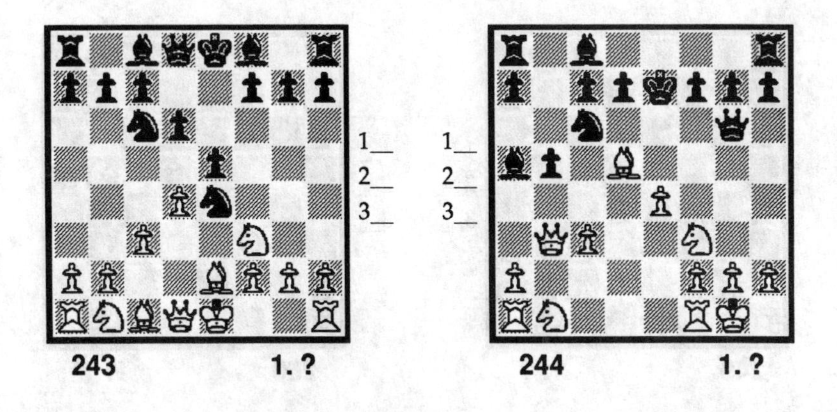

243 1. ? 244 1. ?

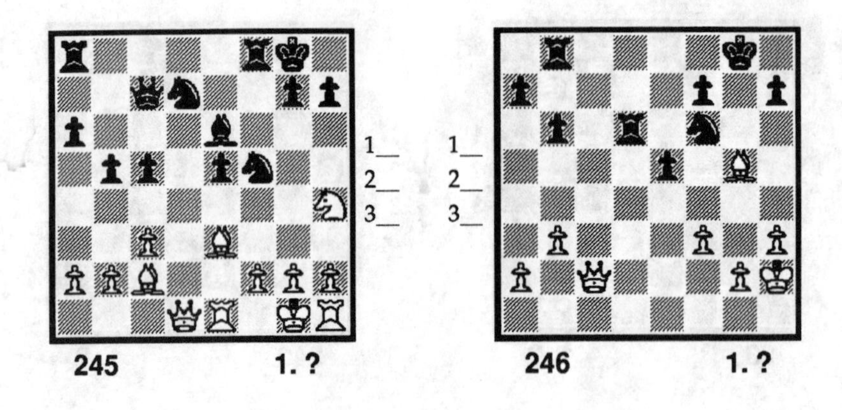

245 1. ?

246 1. ?

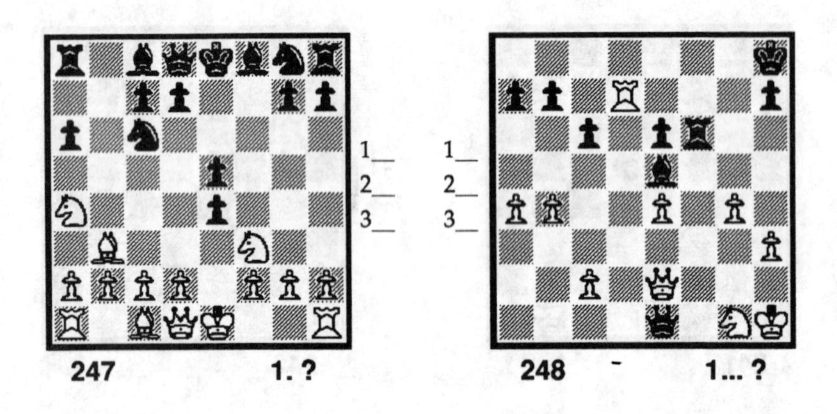

247 1. ?

248 1... ?

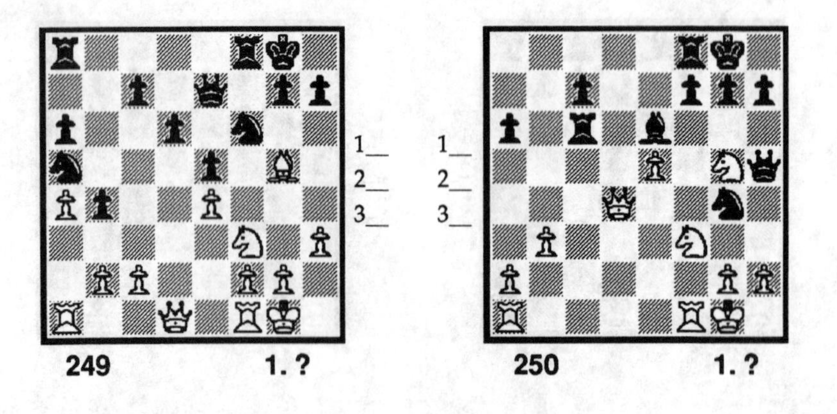

249 1. ?

250 1. ?

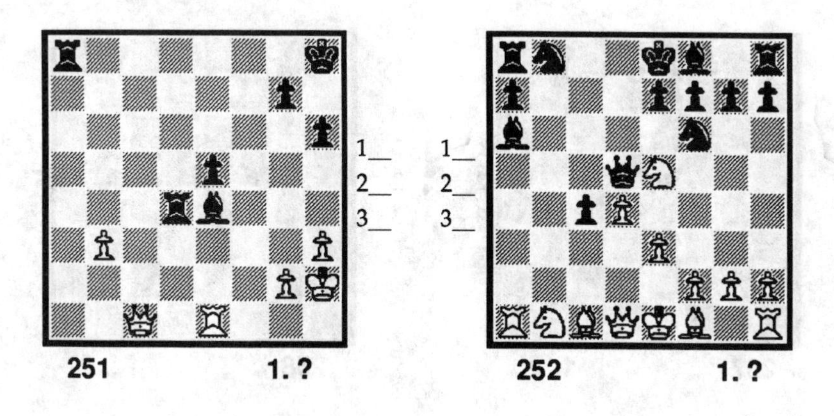
1__
2__
3__
1__
2__
3__
251
1. ?
252
1. ?

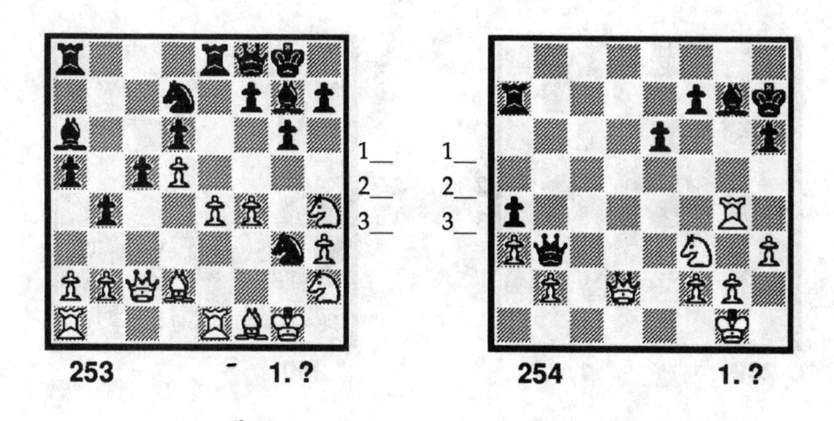
1__
2__
3__
1__
2__
3__
253
1. ?
254
1. ?

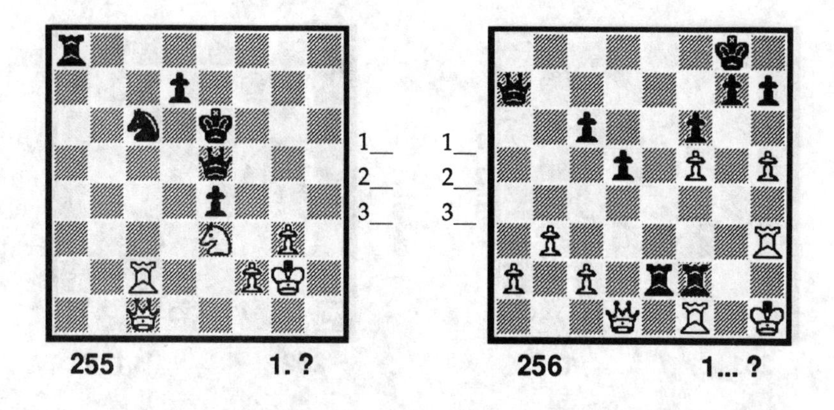
1__
2__
3__
1__
2__
3__
255
1. ?
256
1... ?

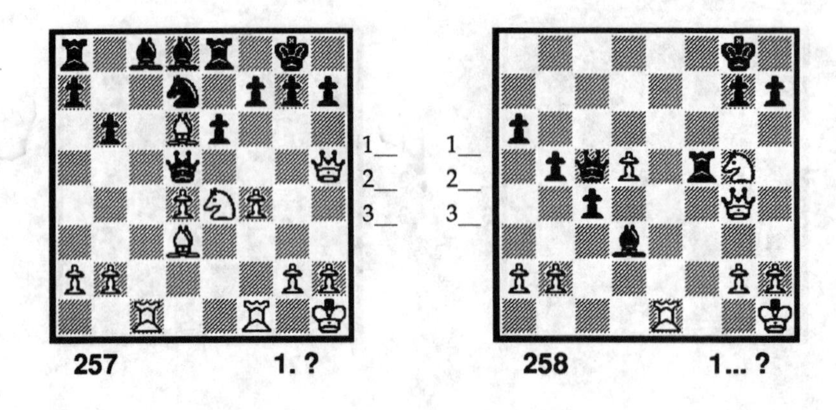

257 1. ?

258 1... ?

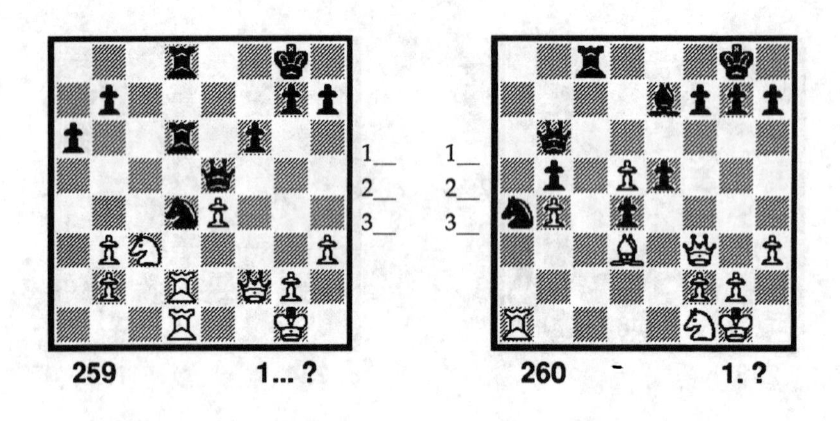

259 1... ?

260 1. ?

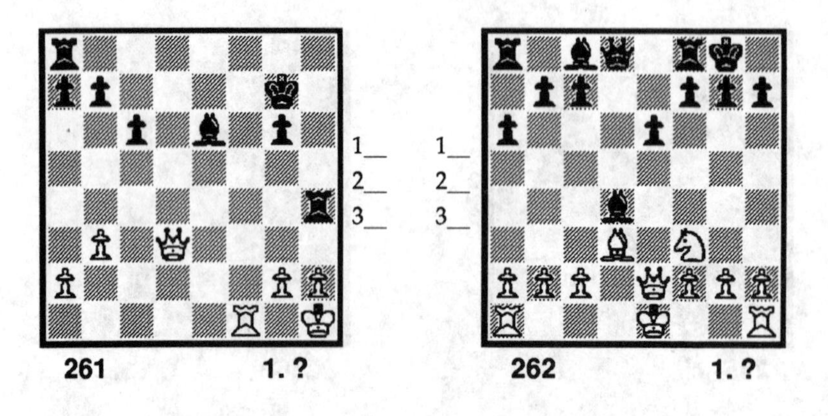

261 1. ?

262 1. ?

CHAPTER 6

ATTRACTION

This device is usually employed to attract an enemy piece onto an unfavorable square. Sometimes this implies that the piece being so attracted is placed under attack. The actual attraction is usually accomplished by a forcing sacrifice. Often a sacrifice will attract the King, exposing it to attack. One of the most famous types of attraction occurs with the so called "Greek Gift" sacrifice of a Bishop at h7 (Bxh7+, or with Black, ...Bxh2+). The attraction motif occurs quite frequently and careful analysis is suggested.

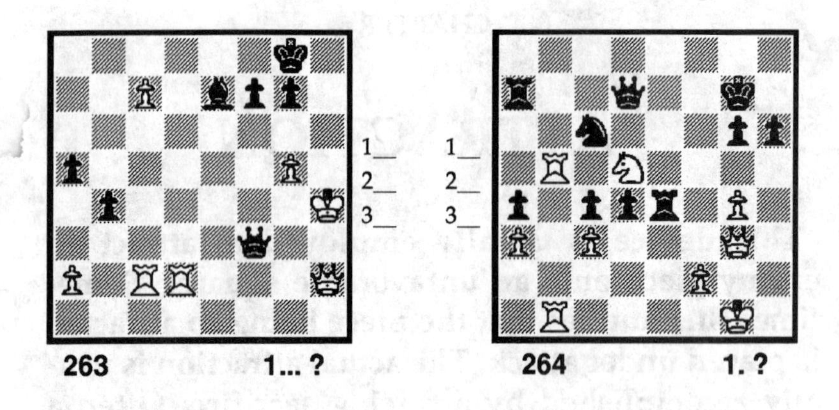
1__
2__
3__
1__
2__
3__
263
1... ?
264
1. ?

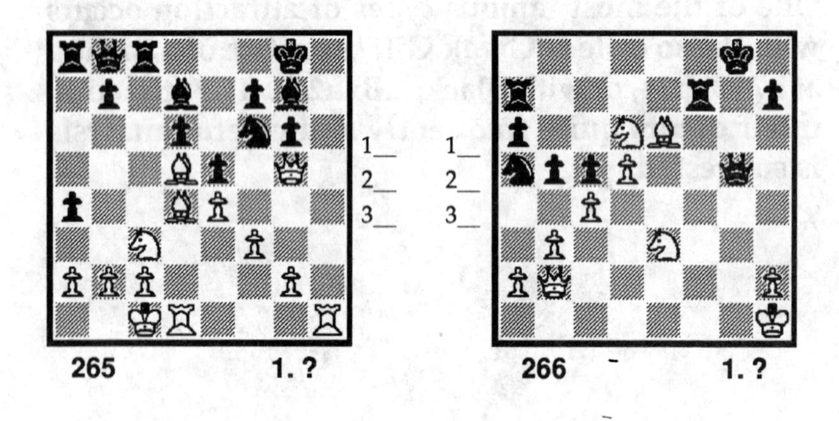
1__
2__
3__
1__
2__
3__
265
1. ?
266
1. ?

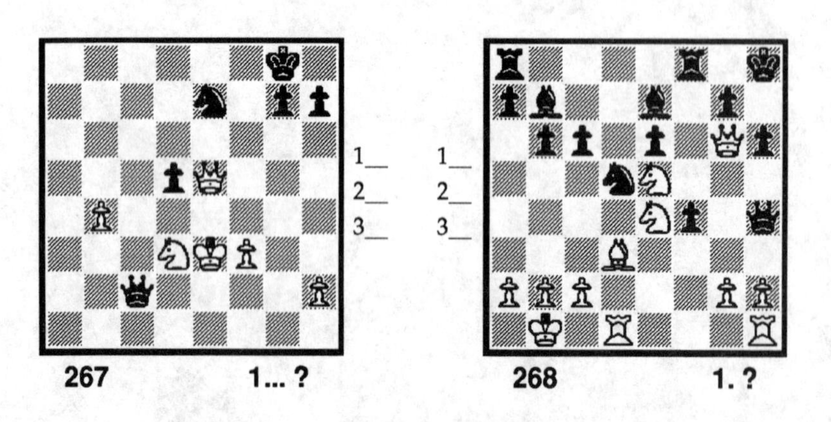
1__
2__
3__
1__
2__
3__
267
1... ?
268
1. ?

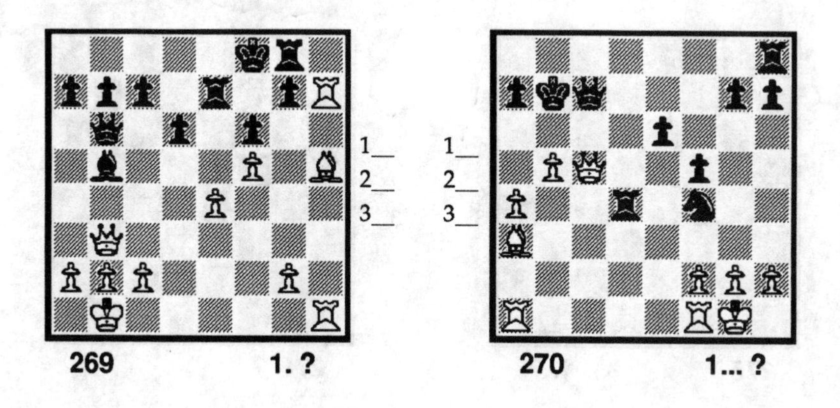
269 1. ?
270 1... ?

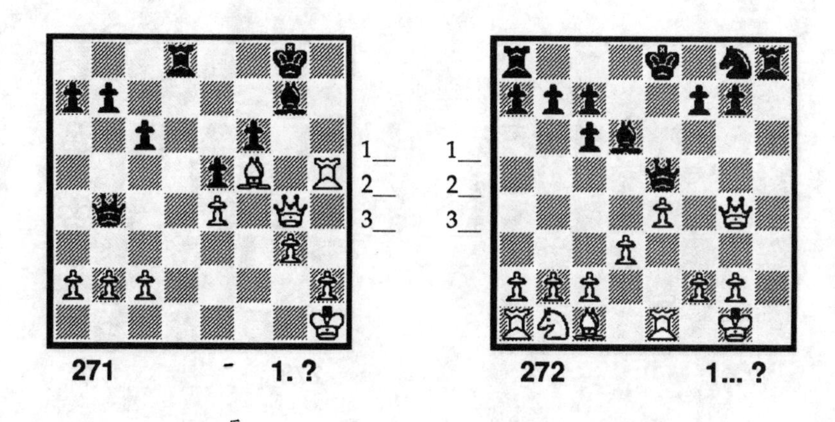
271 1. ?
272 1... ?

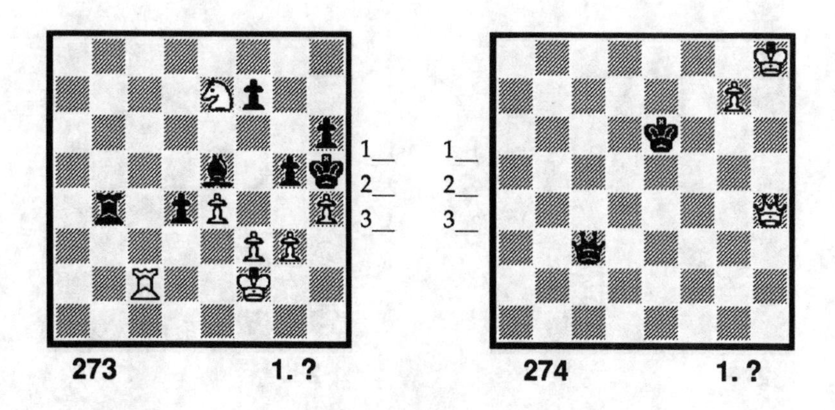
273 1. ?
274 1. ?

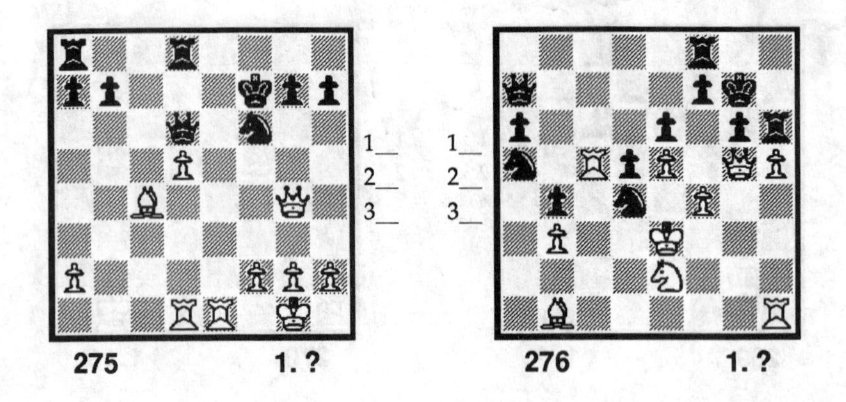

275 **1. ?**

276 **1. ?**

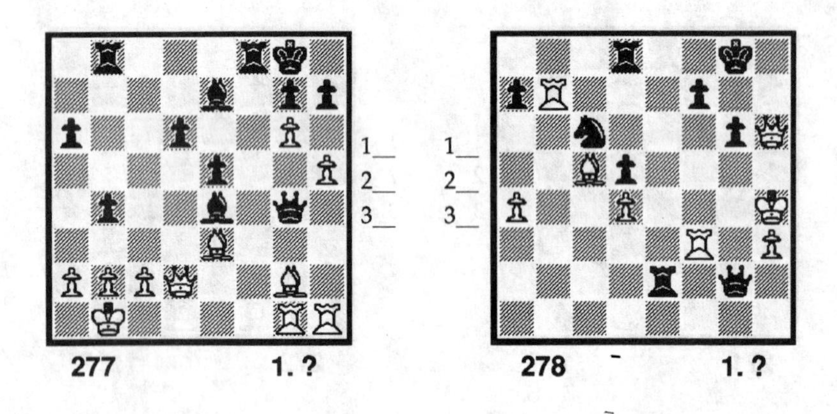

277 **1. ?**

278 **1. ?**

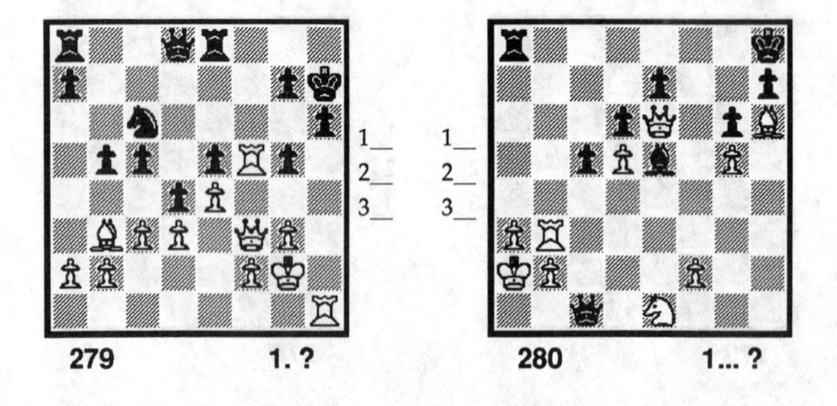

279 **1. ?**

280 **1... ?**

CHAPTER 7

CLEARANCE

This tactic is used to clear a square or uncover a line (rank, file or diagonal) in order for an effective follow-up to take advantage of the newly cleared square or squares. Very often the piece which clears the way for the follow-up actions of another will sacrifice itself in the process. If this sacrifice involves an attack on the enemy King, then the effect is intensified.

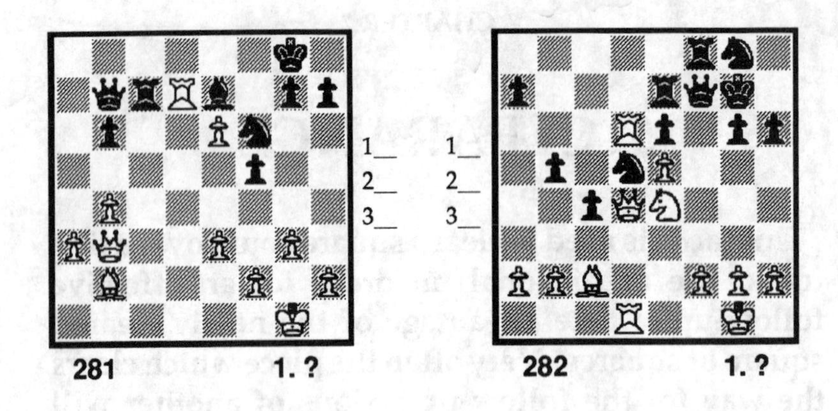
1__ 2__ 3__

1__ 2__ 3__

281 1. ?

282 1. ?

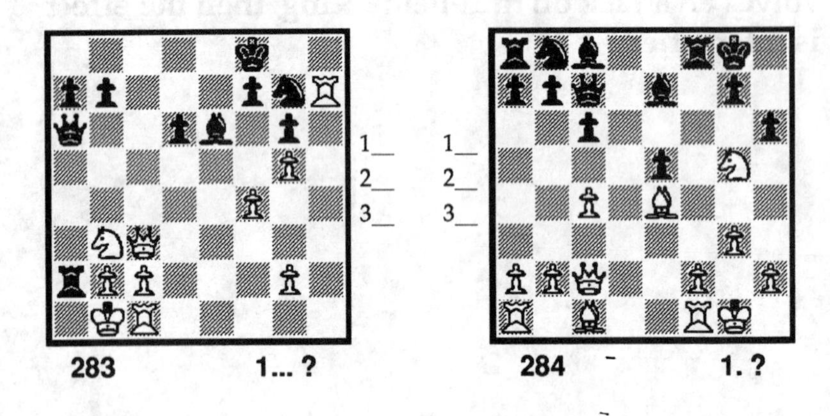
1__ 2__ 3__

1__ 2__ 3__

283 1... ?

284 1. ?

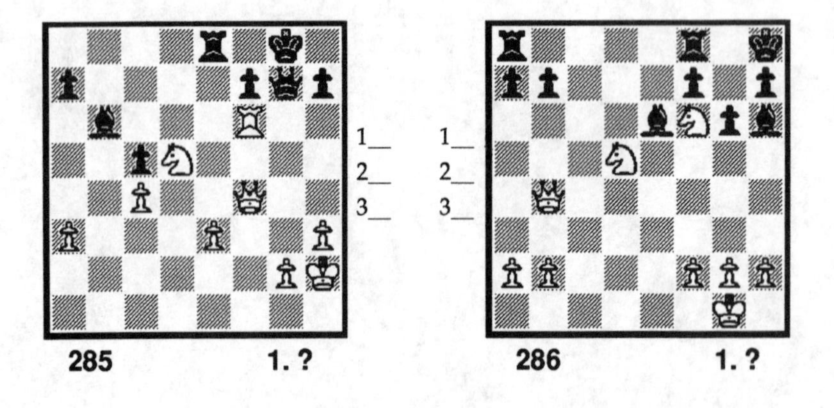
1__ 2__ 3__

1__ 2__ 3__

285 1. ?

286 1. ?

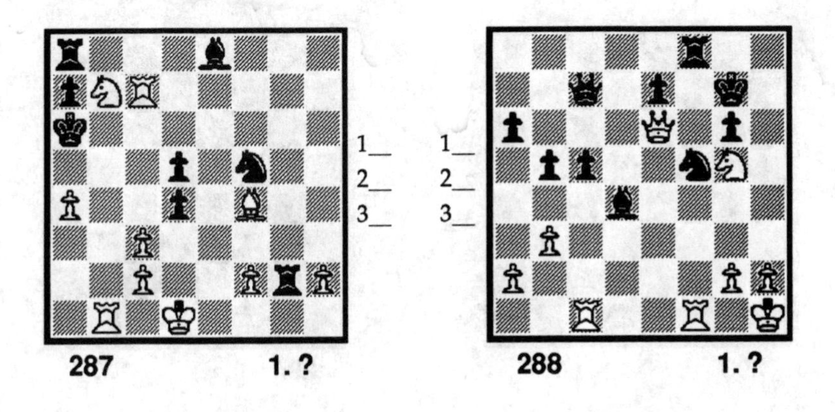

287 **1. ?** **288** **1. ?**

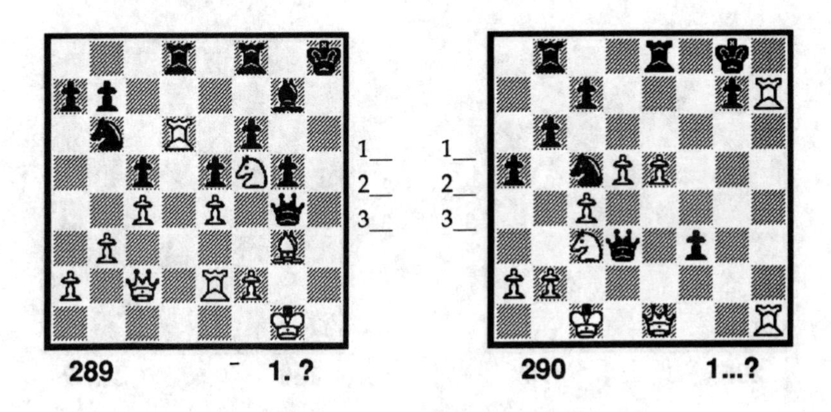

289 **1. ?** **290** **1...?**

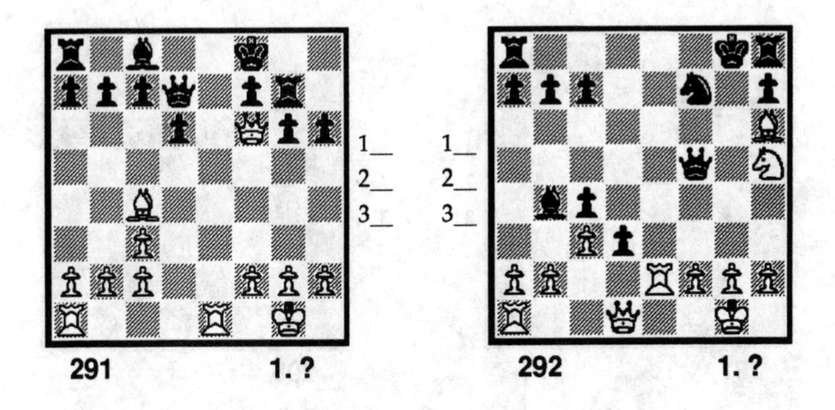

291 **1. ?** **292** **1. ?**

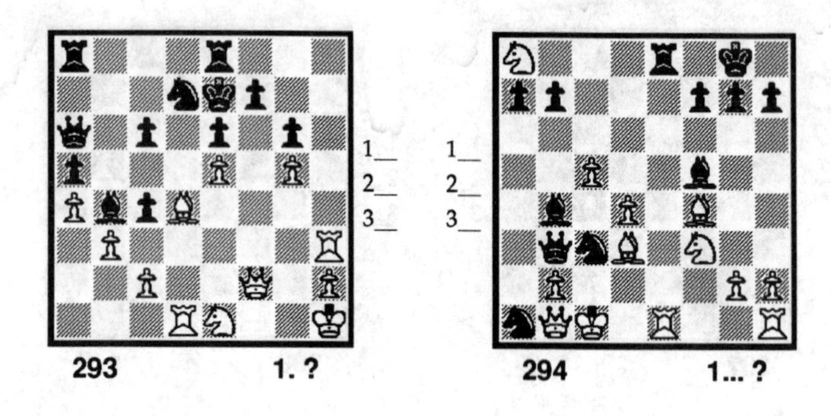

293 1. ? 294 1... ?

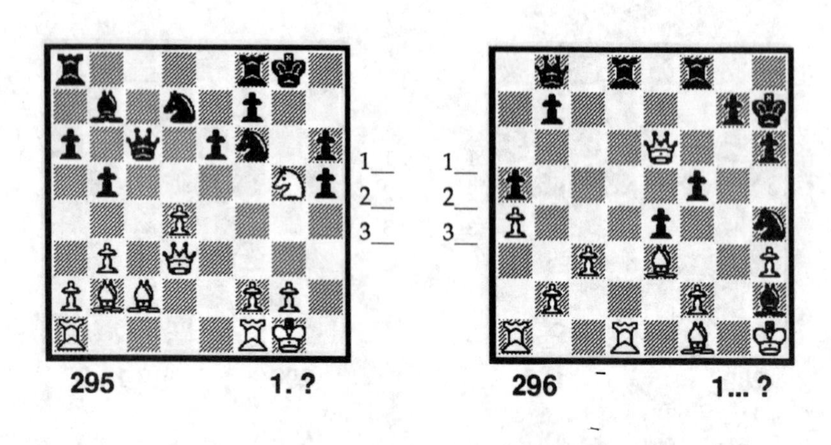

295 1. ? 296 1... ?

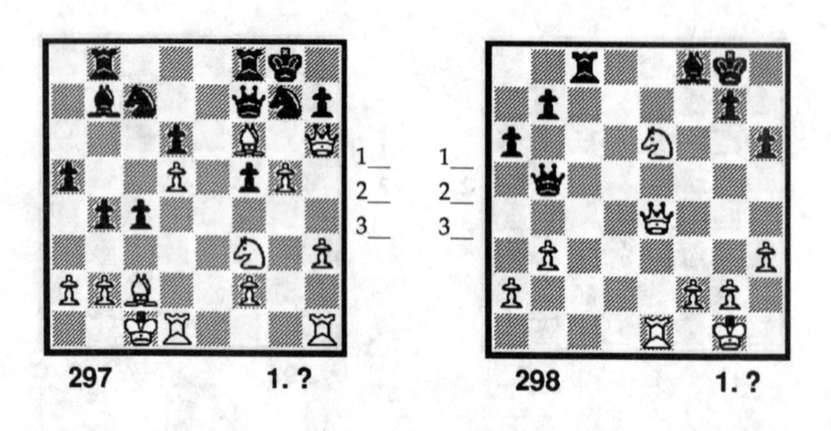

297 1. ? 298 1. ?

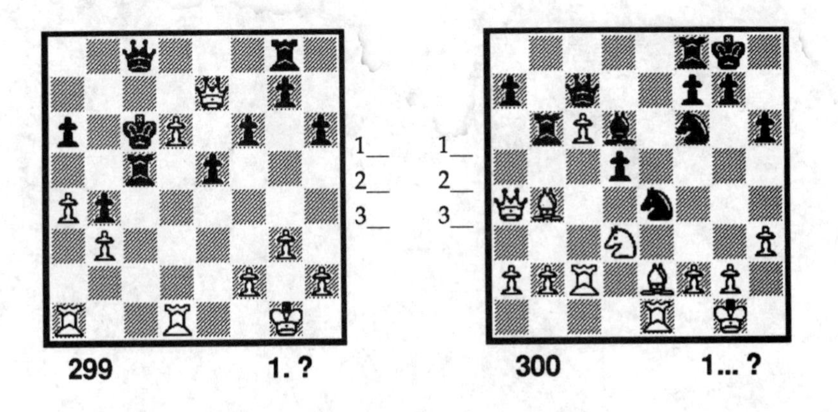

299 1. ?

300 1... ?

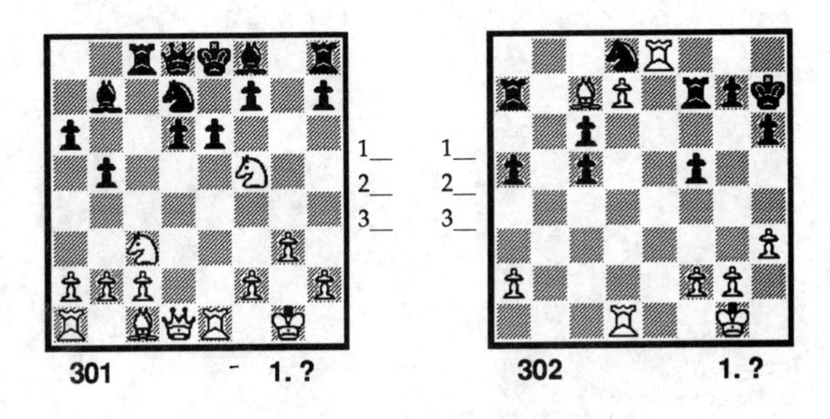

301 1. ?

302 1. ?

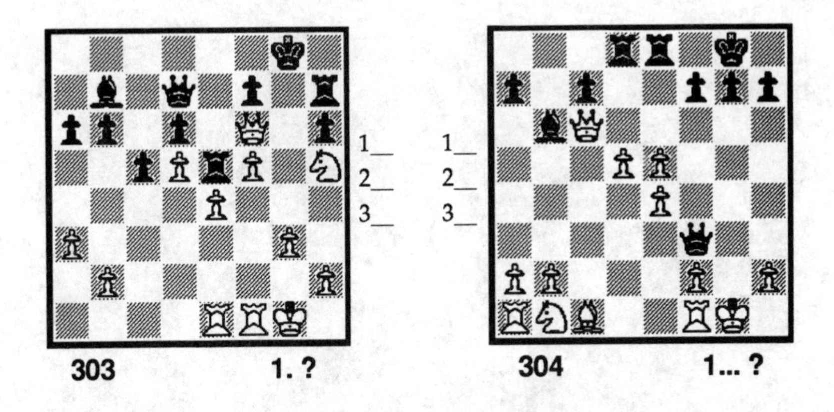

303 1. ?

304 1... ?

CHAPTER 8

OVERLOADING

Overloading involves the exploitation of an enemy unit which must protect at least two other important pieces (or squares). The object of the attacker is to force the overloaded defending piece to relinquish its necessary defensive functions. Typically this is accomplished by attacking one of the defensive piece's "dependents" and thereby making the defender give up the protection of its other obligation (s). Often the defending piece is forced to leave its home square in order to protect one of its pieces or squares which in turn gives up its protection of another piece or square.

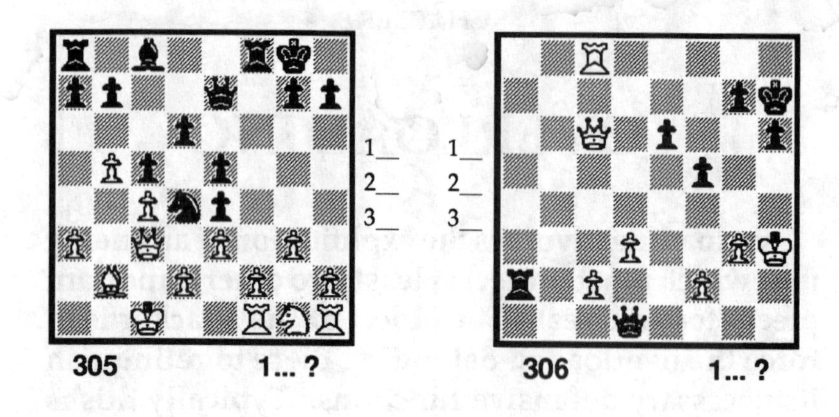

1__
2__
3__
1__
2__
3__
305
1... ?
306
1... ?

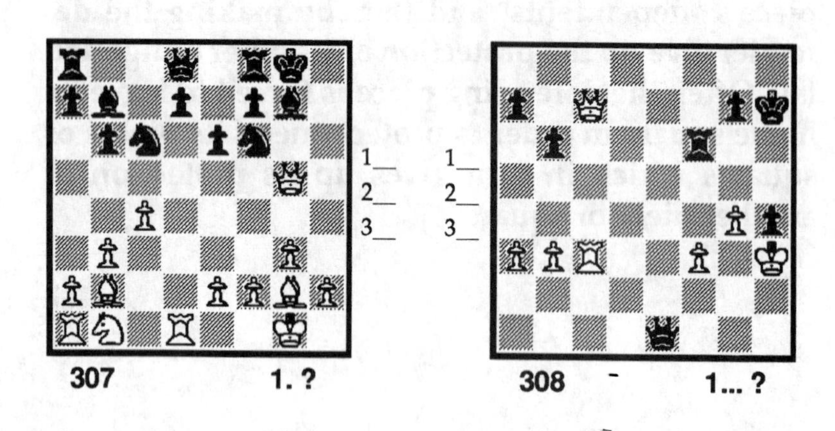

1__
2__
3__
1__
2__
3__
307
1. ?
308
1... ?

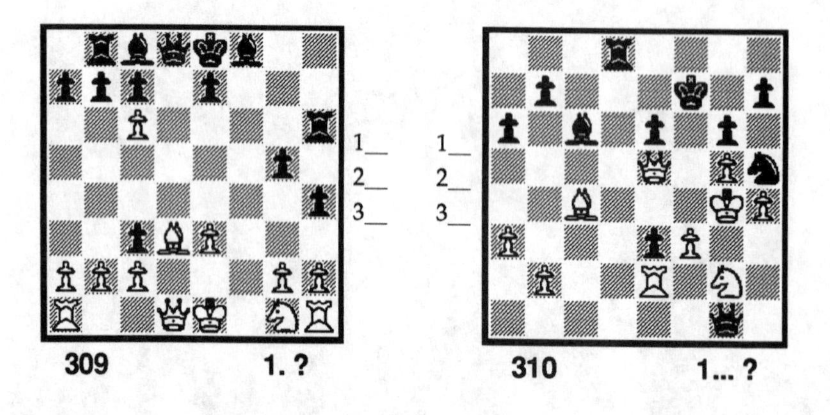

1__
2__
3__
1__
2__
3__
309
1. ?
310
1... ?

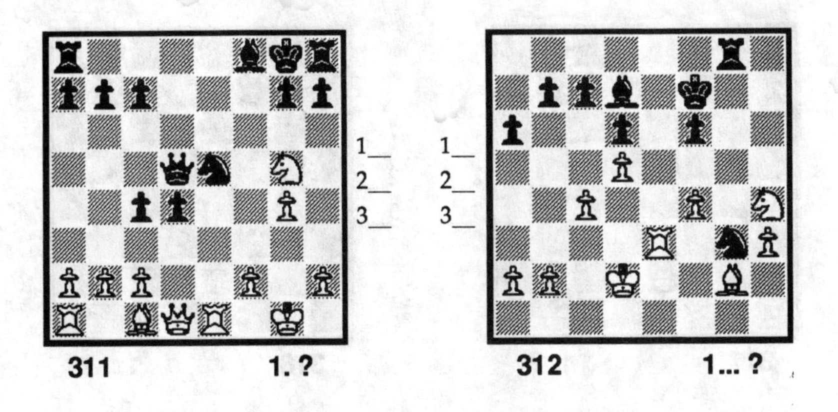

311 1. ?

312 1... ?

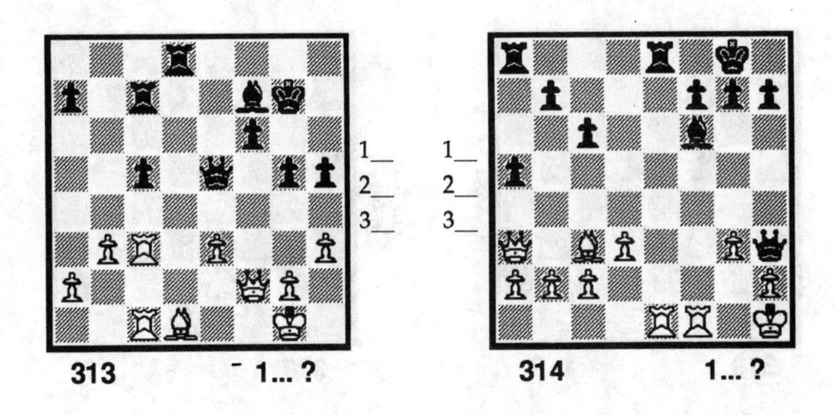

313 1... ?

314 1... ?

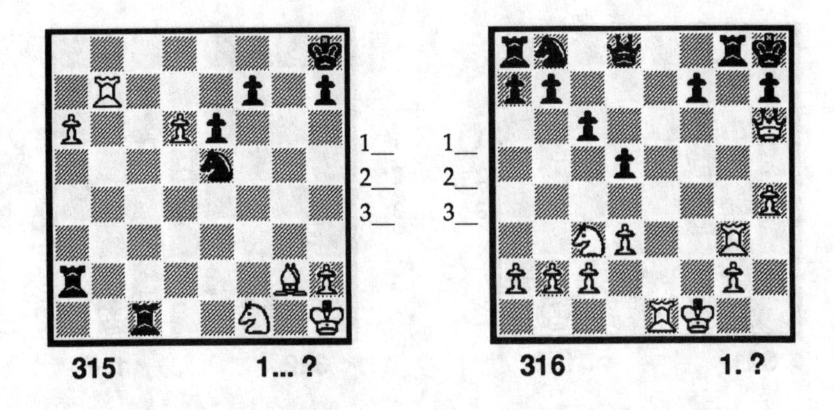

315 1... ?

316 1. ?

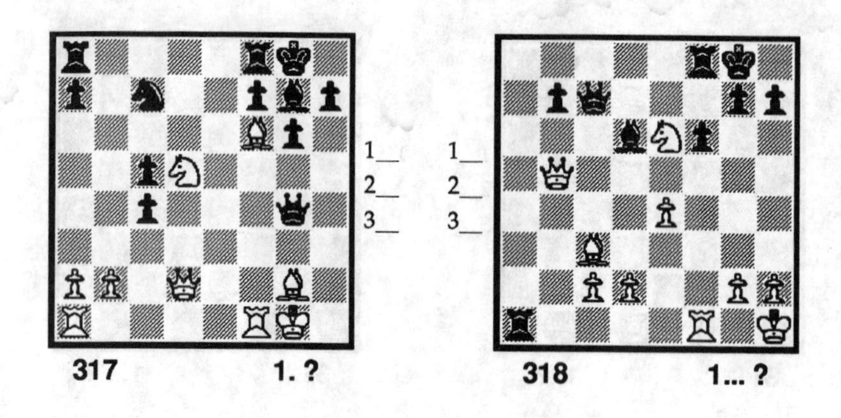

317 1. ? 318 1... ?

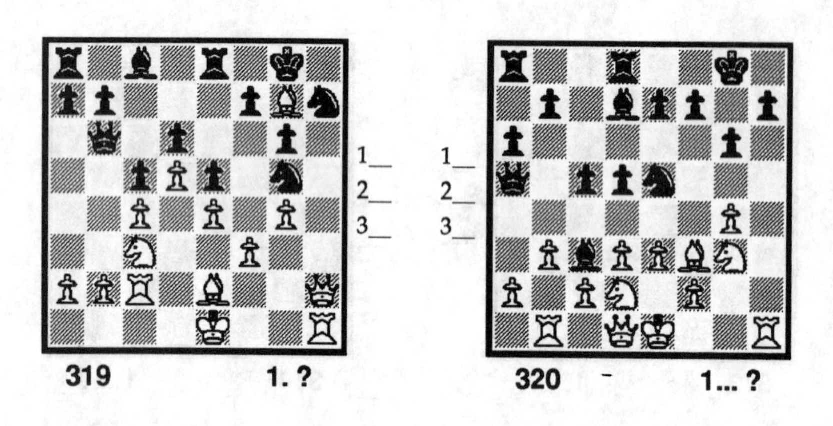

319 1. ? 320 1... ?

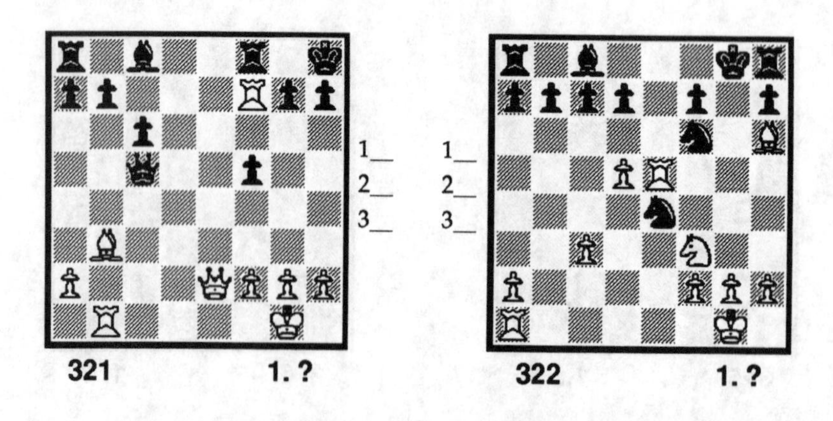

321 1. ? 322 1. ?

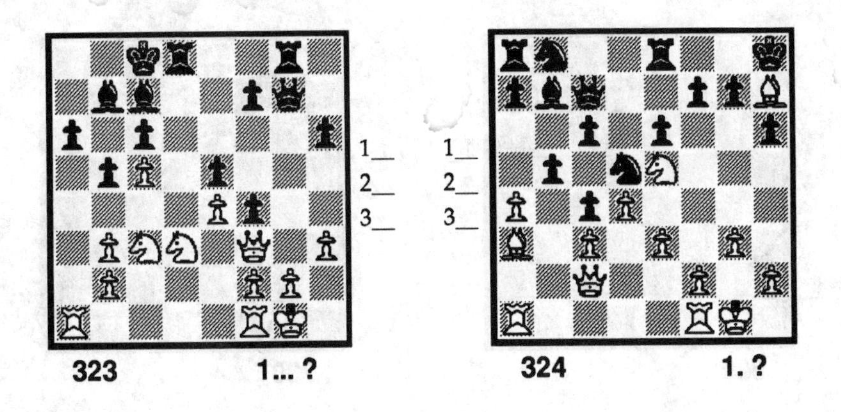

323 1... ?

324 1. ?

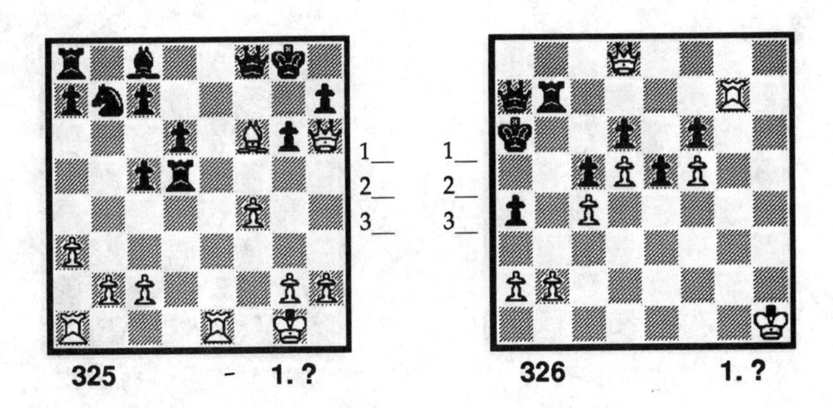

325 1. ?

326 1. ?

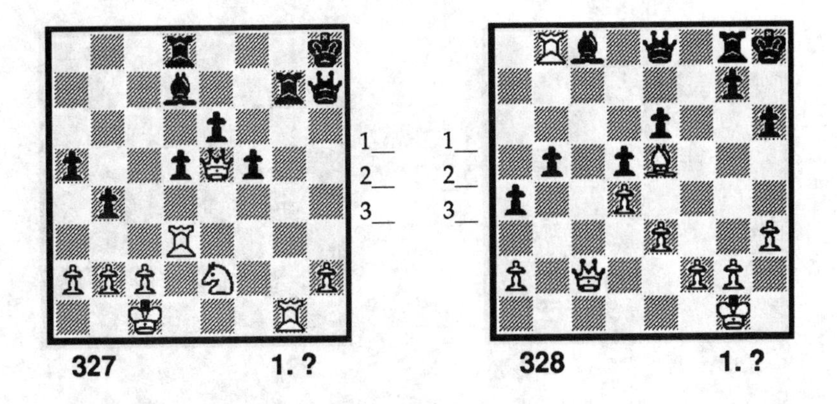

327 1. ?

328 1. ?

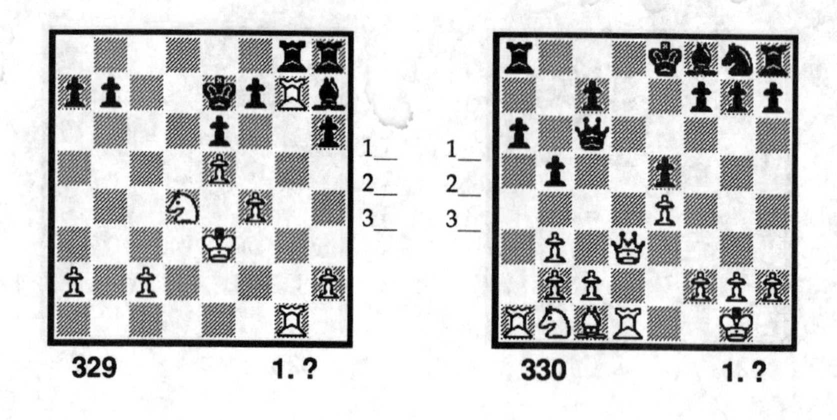

329 1. ? 330 1. ?

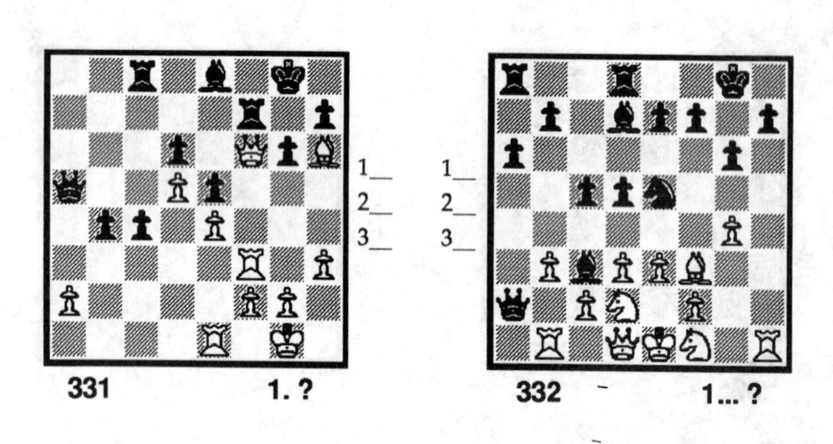

331 1. ? 332 1... ?

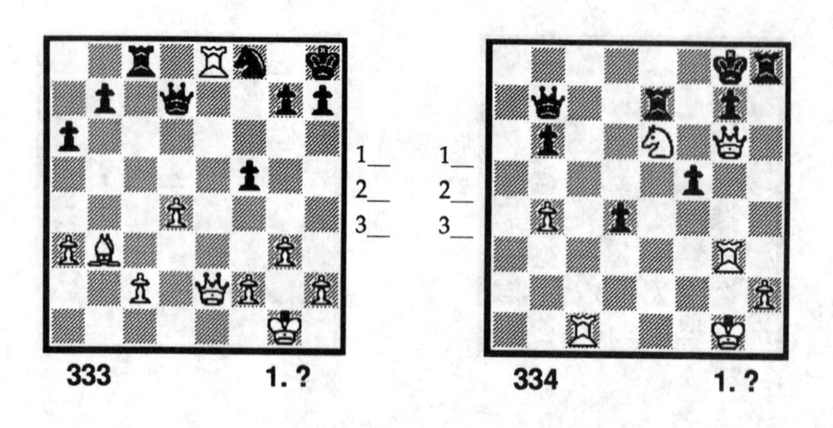

333 1. ? 334 1. ?

CHAPTER 9

DIVERSION

Diversion is a motif in which we divert an enemy piece from an important post. Once the piece is diverted we can then exploit the new setting to attack other vital elements of the opponent's position. Often the diverted piece is charged with protecting another. Its diversion leaves the other piece underdefended and hence vulnerable. This type of operation is also called removing the guard and occurs with great frequency in chess. Close examination of these examples will pay great dividends.

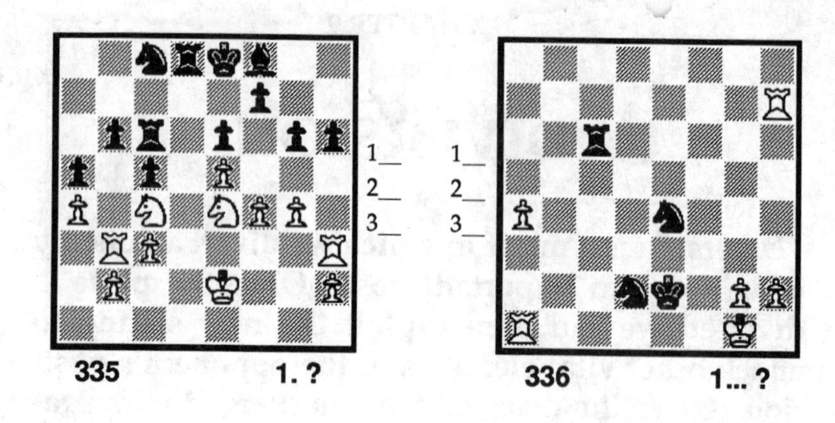
1__
2__
3__
1__
2__
3__
335
1. ?
336
1... ?

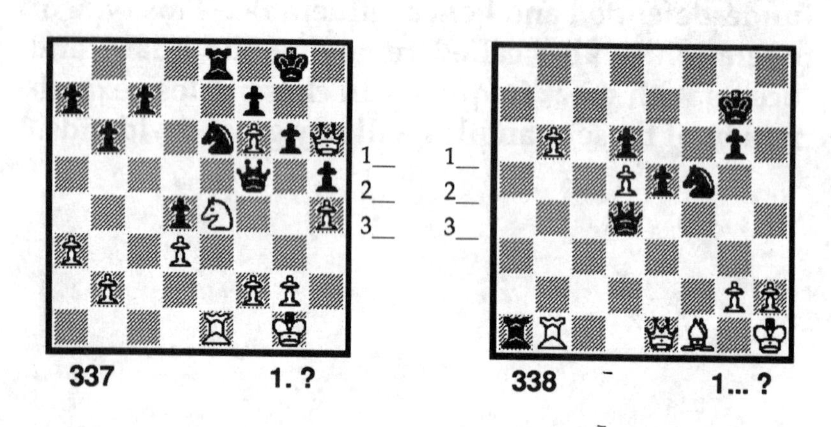
1__
2__
3__
1__
2__
3__
337
1. ?
338
1... ?

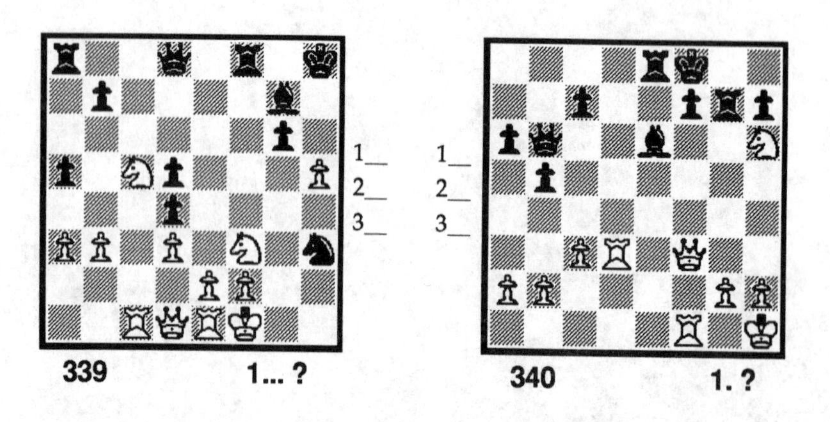
1__
2__
3__
1__
2__
3__
339
1... ?
340
1. ?

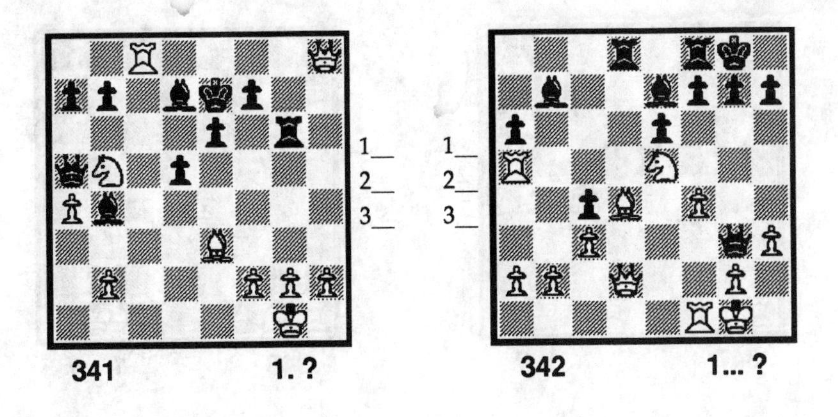

341 1. ?

342 1... ?

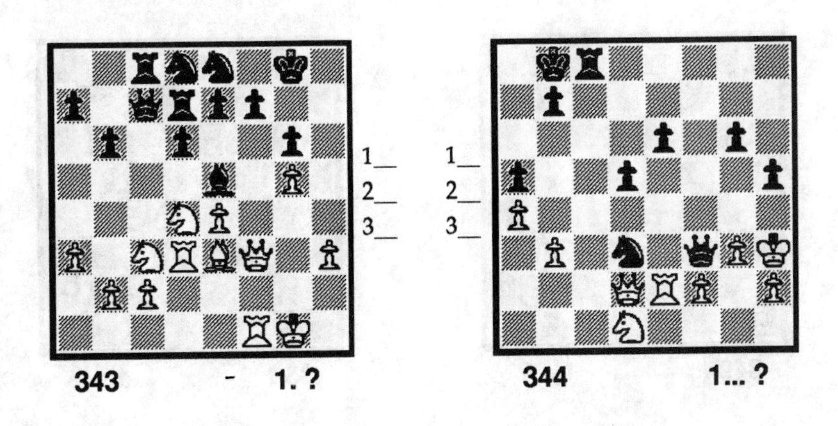

343 1. ?

344 1... ?

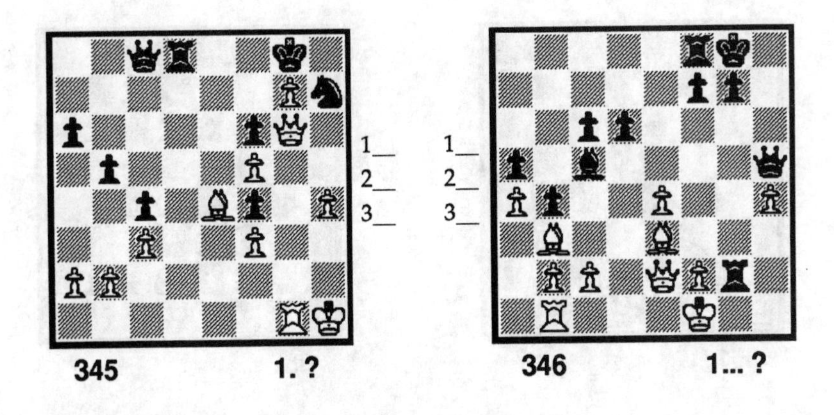

345 1. ?

346 1... ?

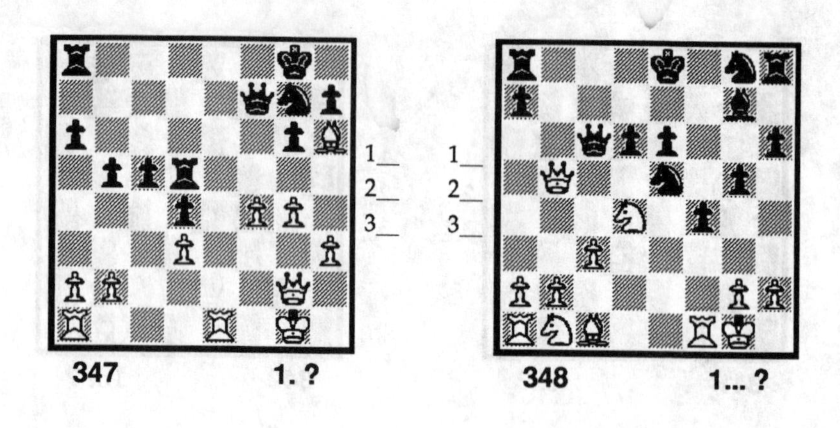

347 1. ?

348 1... ?

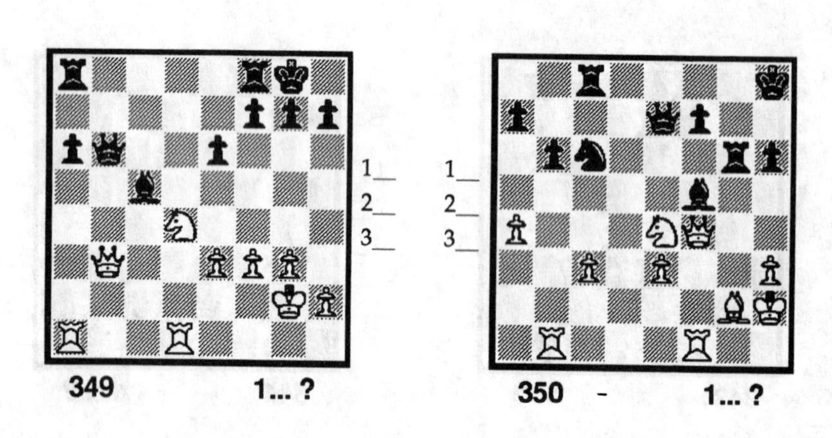

349 1... ?

350 1... ?

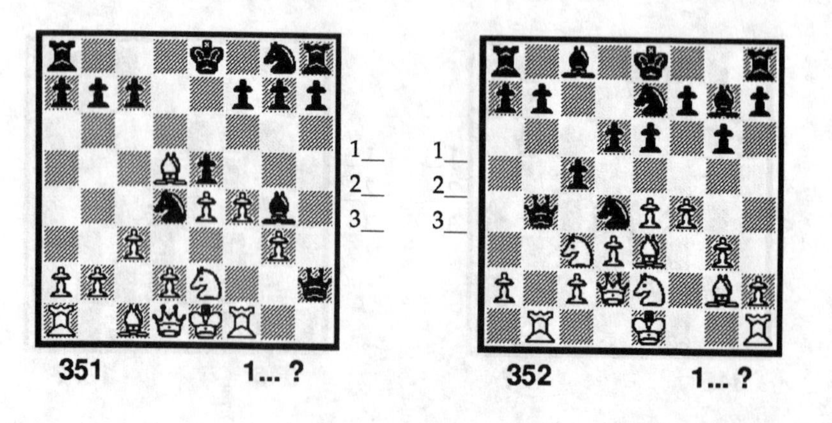

351 1... ?

352 1... ?

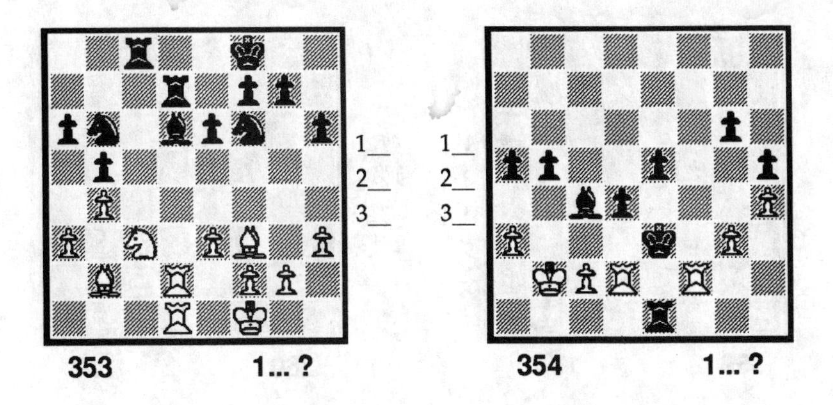

353 1... ?

354 1... ?

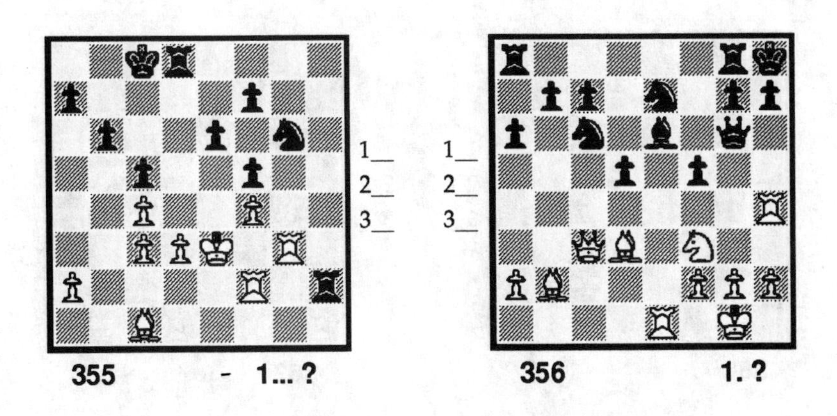

355 1... ?

356 1. ?

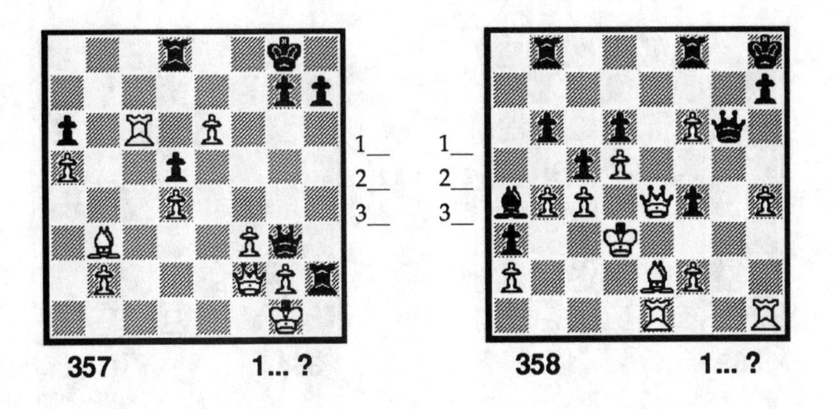

357 1... ?

358 1... ?

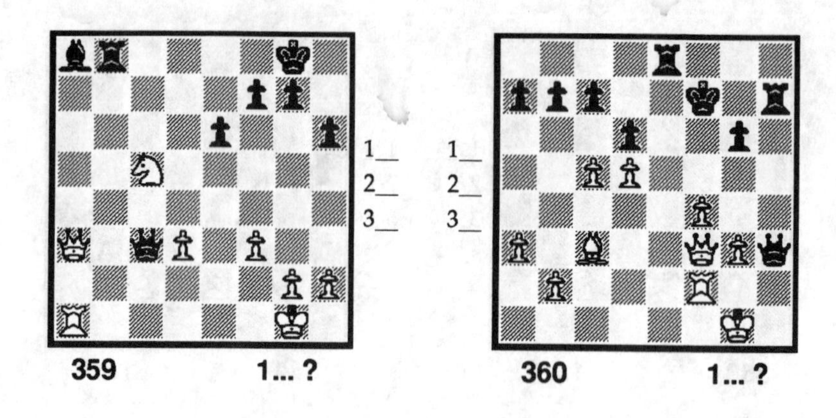

359 1... ?

360 1... ?

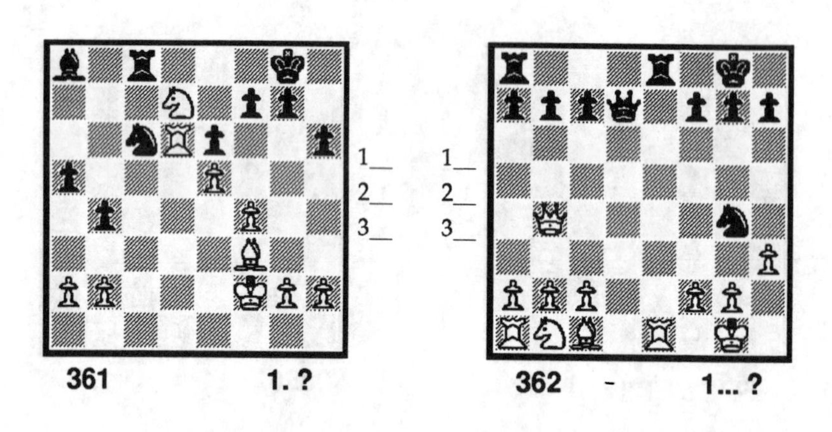

361 1. ?

362 1... ?

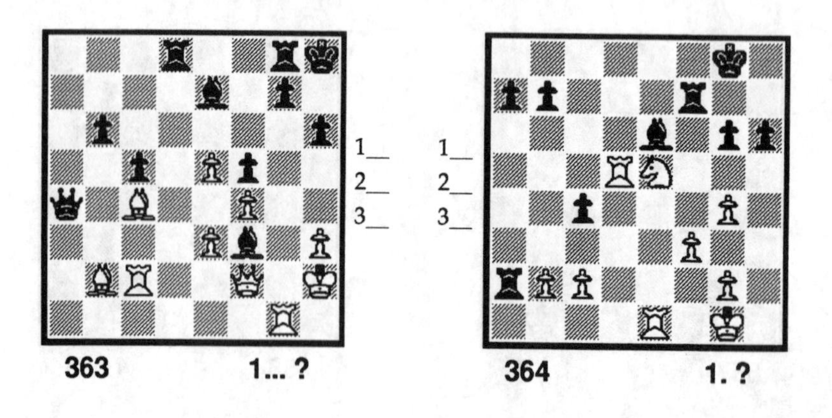

363 1... ?

364 1. ?

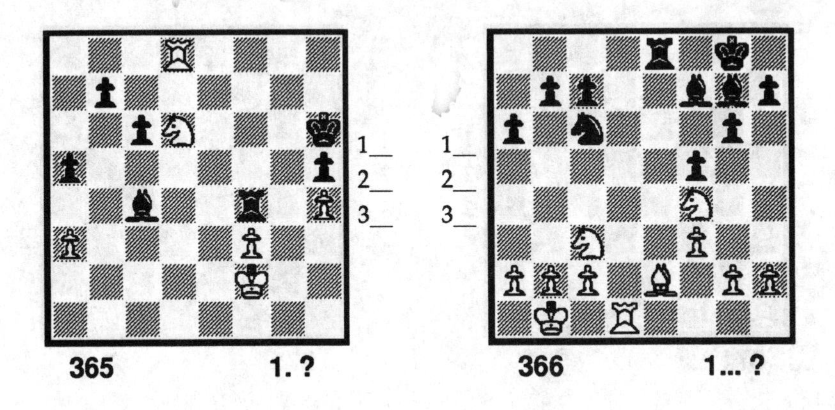
1__
2__
3__
1__
2__
3__
365
1. ?
366
1... ?

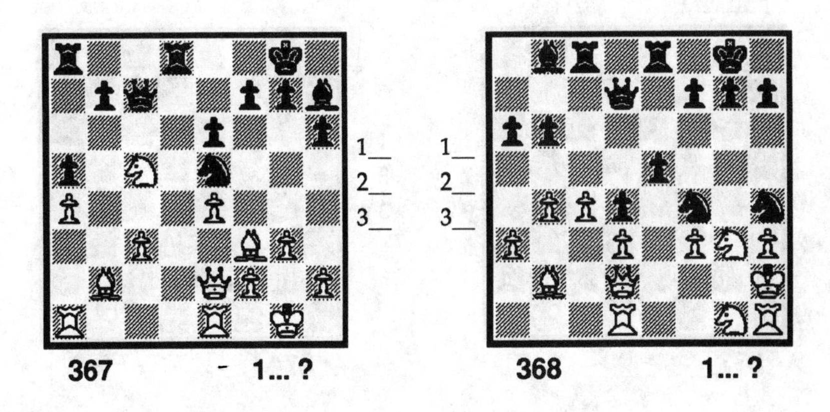
1__
2__
3__
1__
2__
3__
367
1... ?
368
1... ?

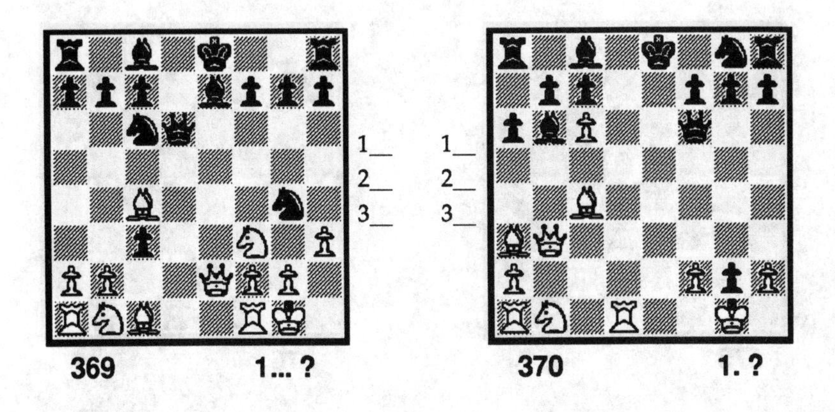
1__
2__
3__
1__
2__
3__
369
1... ?
370
1. ?

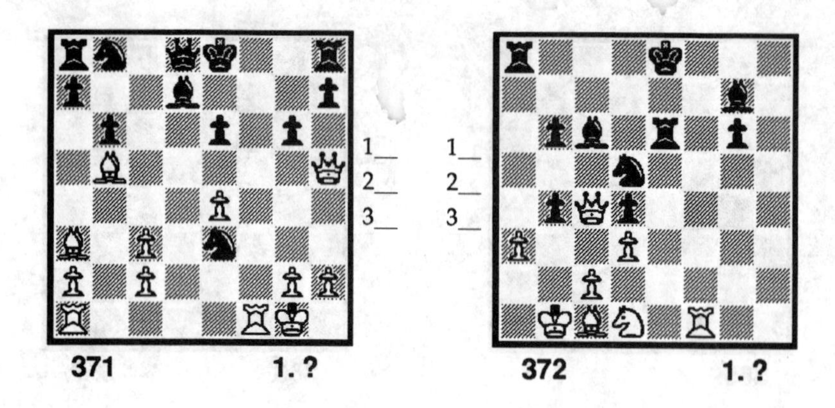
1__
2__
3__
1__
2__
3__
371
1. ?
372
1. ?

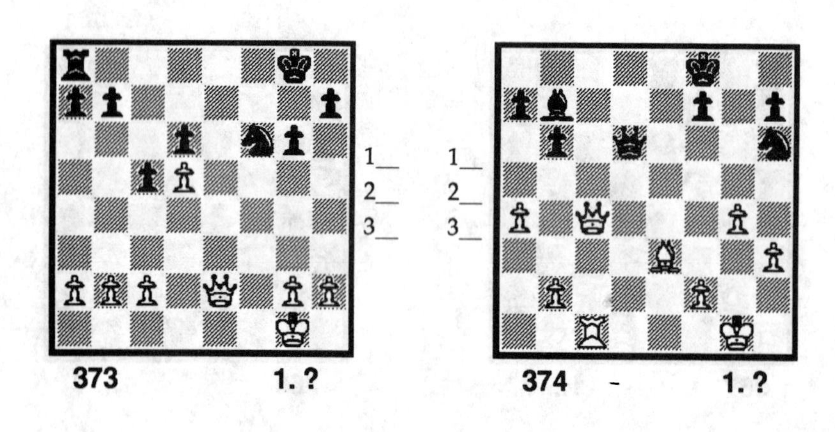
1__
2__
3__
1__
2__
3__
373
1. ?
374
1. ?

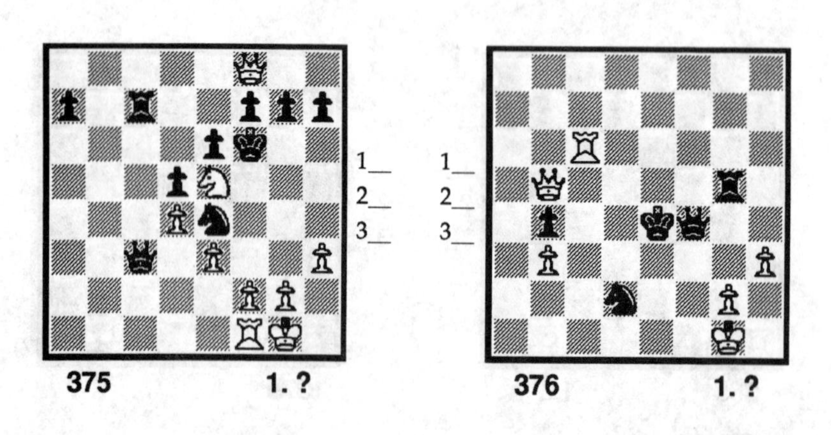
1__
2__
3__
1__
2__
3__
375
1. ?
376
1. ?

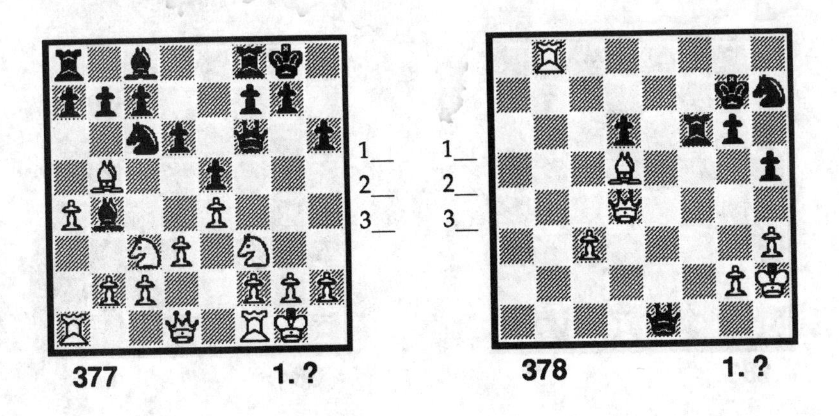

377 **1. ?**

378 **1. ?**

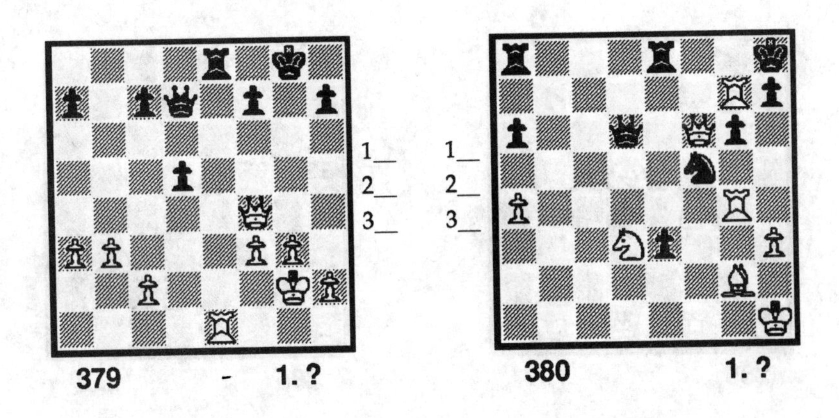

379 **1. ?**

380 **1. ?**

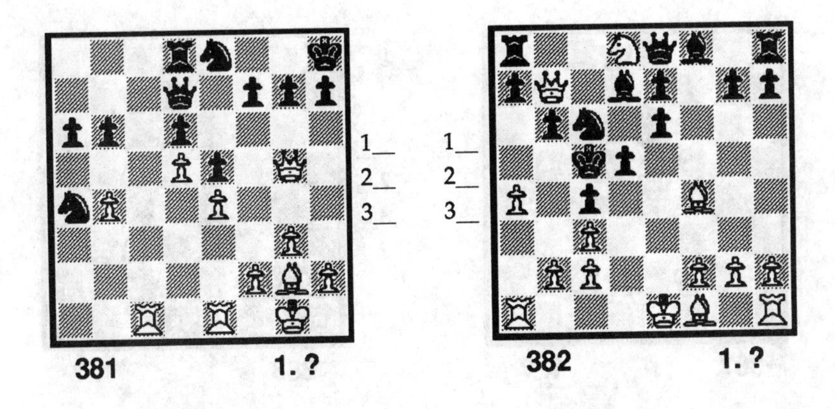

381 **1. ?**

382 **1. ?**

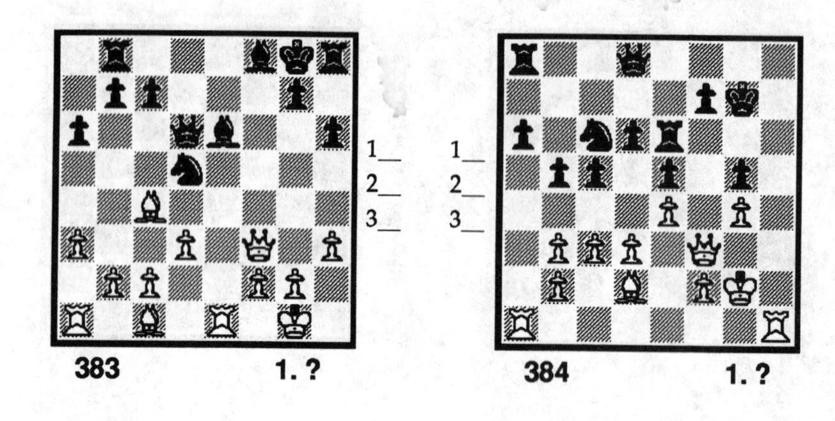
383 1. ?
1__ 2__ 3__
384 1. ?
1__ 2__ 3__

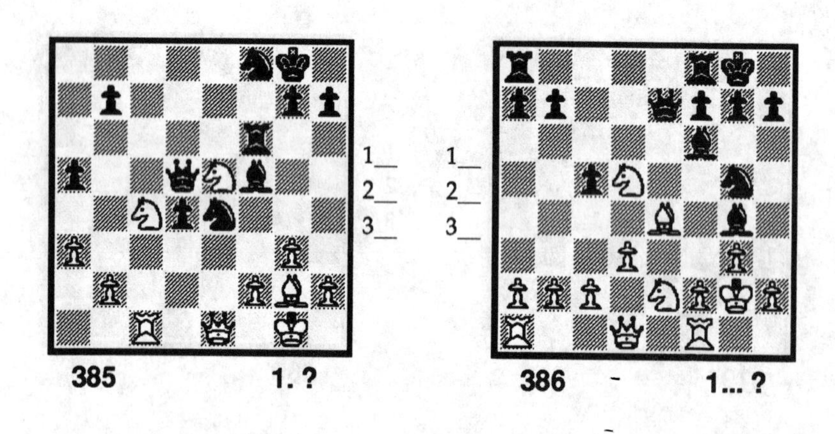
385 1. ?
1__ 2__ 3__
386 1... ?
1__ 2__ 3__

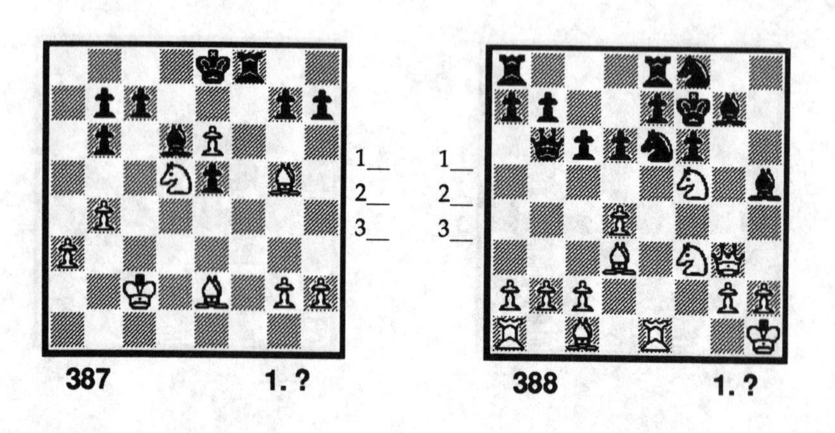
387 1. ?
1__ 2__ 3__
388 1. ?
1__ 2__ 3__

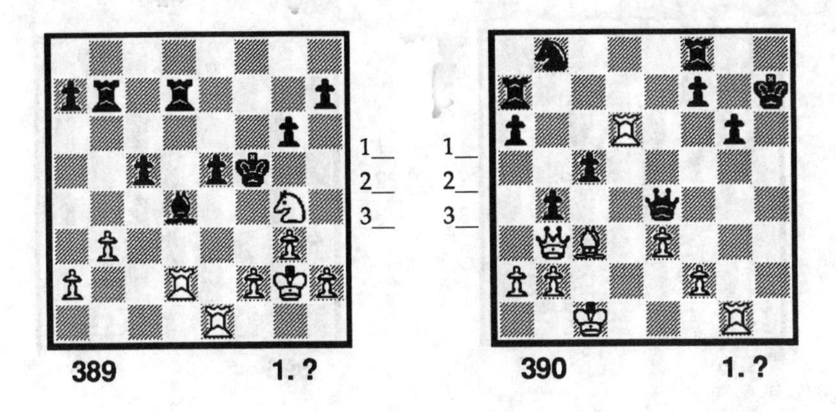
1__ 2__ 3__
1__ 2__ 3__

389 1. ?

390 1. ?

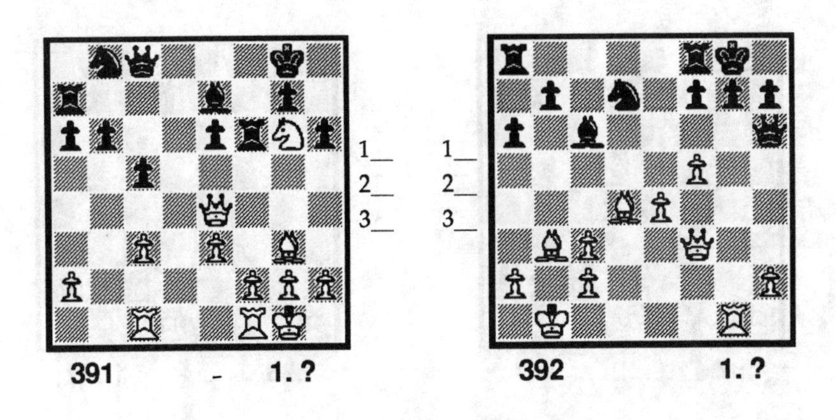
1__ 2__ 3__
1__ 2__ 3__

391 - 1. ?

392 1. ?

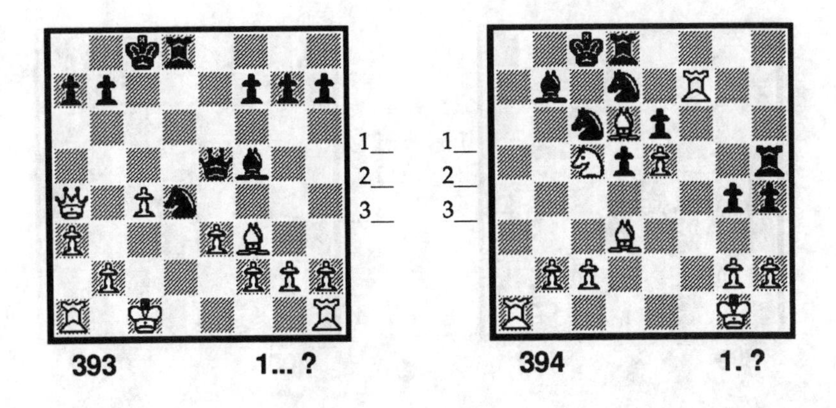
1__ 2__ 3__
1__ 2__ 3__

393 1... ?

394 1. ?

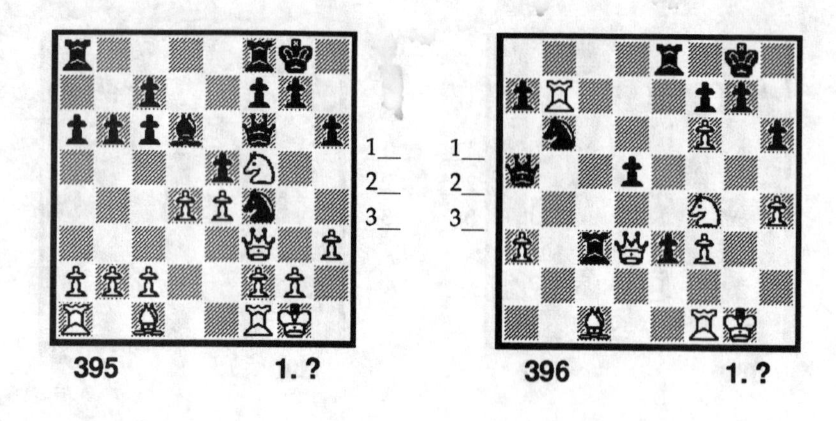

395 1. ?

396 1. ?

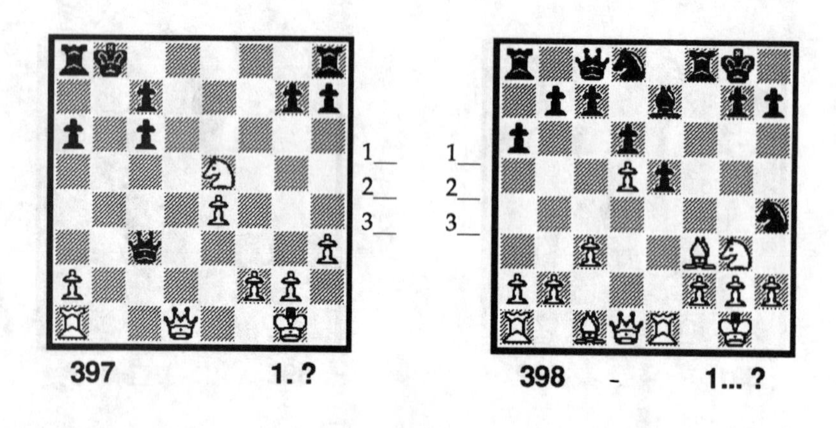

397 1. ?

398 1... ?

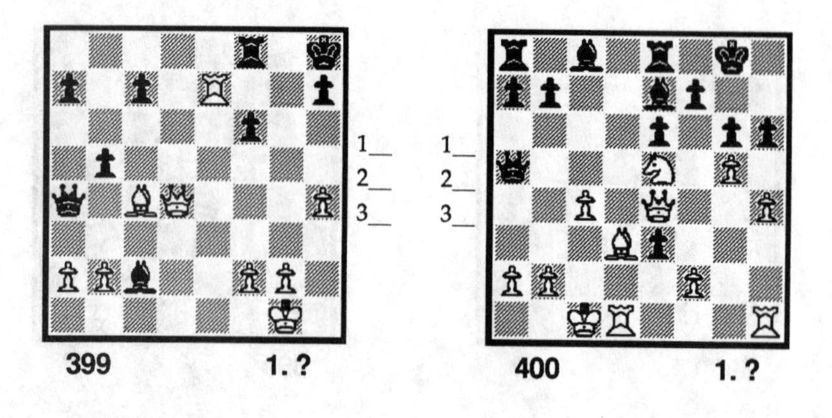

399 1. ?

400 1. ?

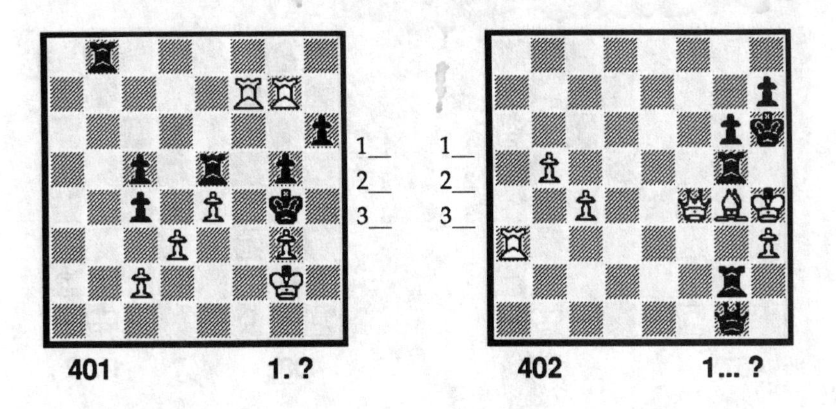
1__
2__
3__
1__
2__
3__
401
1. ?
402
1... ?

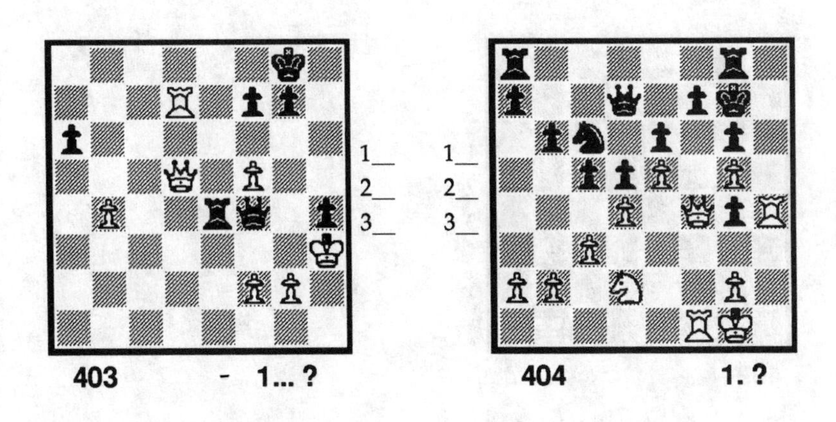
1__
2__
3__
1__
2__
3__
403
1... ?
404
1. ?

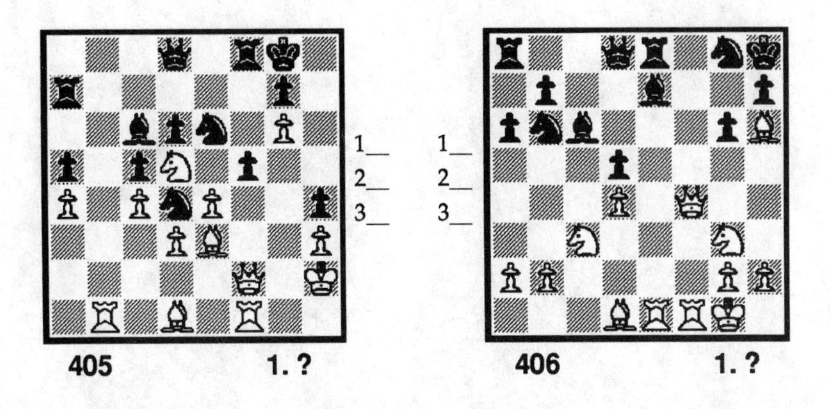
1__
2__
3__
1__
2__
3__
405
1. ?
406
1. ?

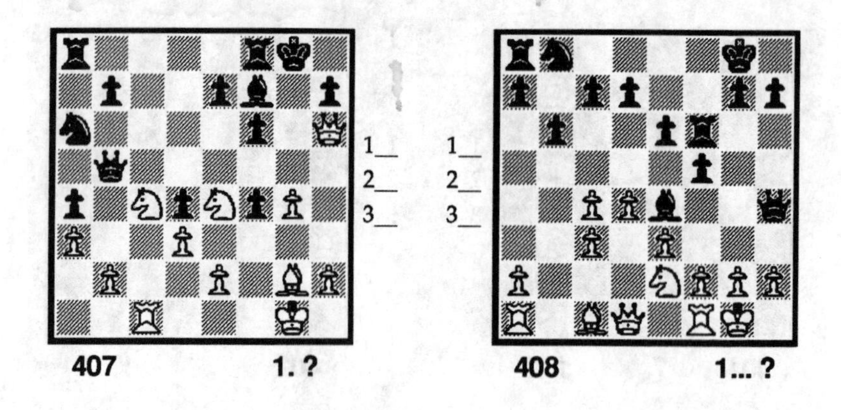

407 1. ?

408 1... ?

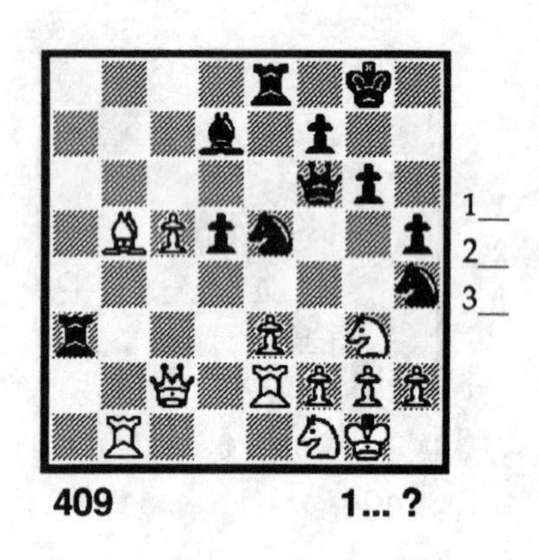

409 1... ?

CHAPTER 10

BACK RANK

Combinations based on the vulnerable back rank are made possible by the targeted King being hemmed in by his own pawns and/or pieces. The simplest examples of this type of combination occur when the back rank is left without a Queen or Rook to help defend against invading heavy pieces. As some of these examples will show, even an apparently well-guarded back rank can often be exploited by the resourceful attacker.

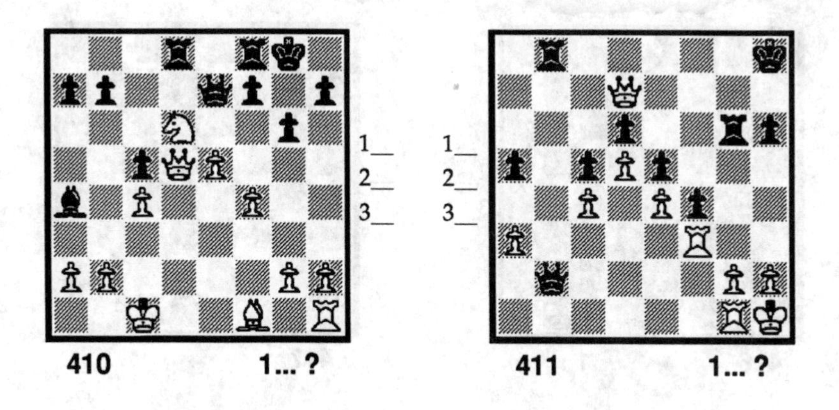
1__
2__
3__
1__
2__
3__
410
1... ?
411
1... ?

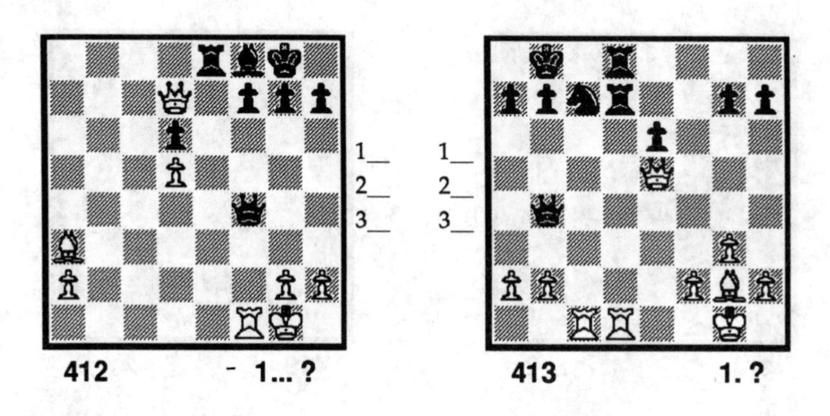
1__
2__
3__
1__
2__
3__
412
1... ?
413
1. ?

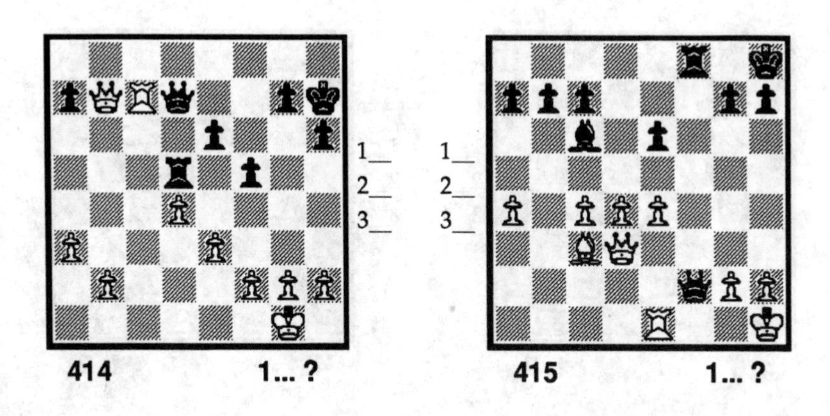
1__
2__
3__
1__
2__
3__
414
1... ?
415
1... ?

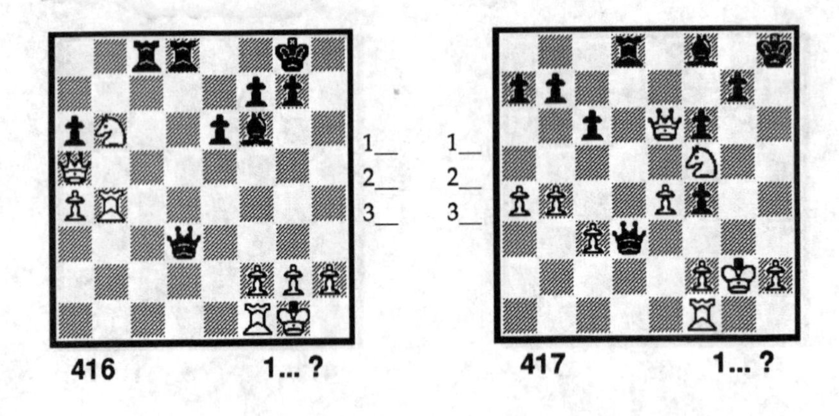

416 1... ?

417 1... ?

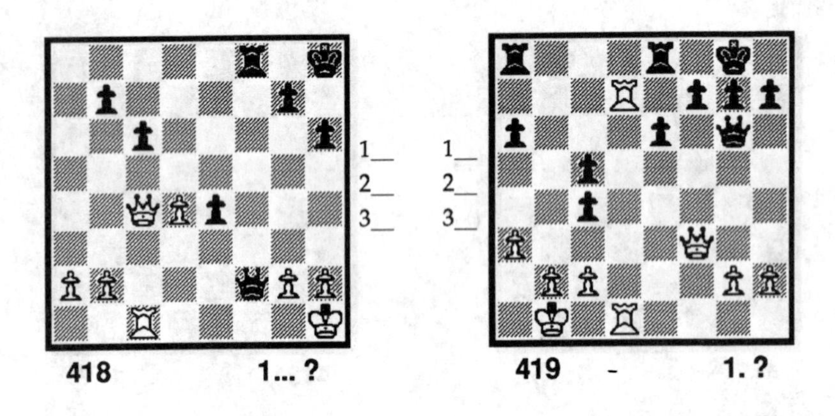

418 1... ?

419 1. ?

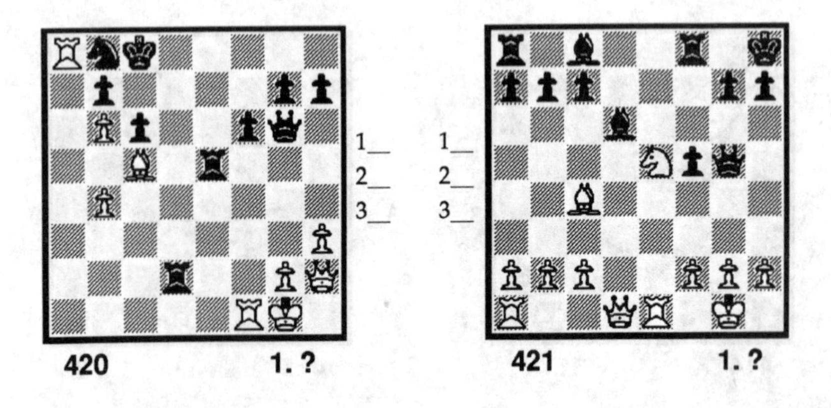

420 1. ?

421 1. ?

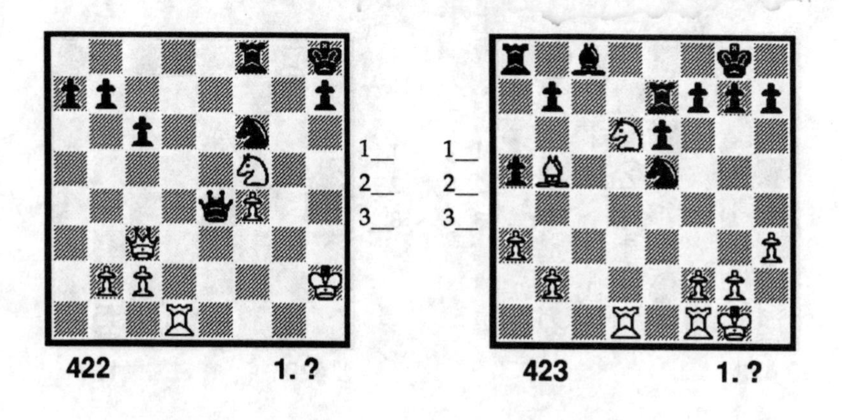

422 1. ?

423 1. ?

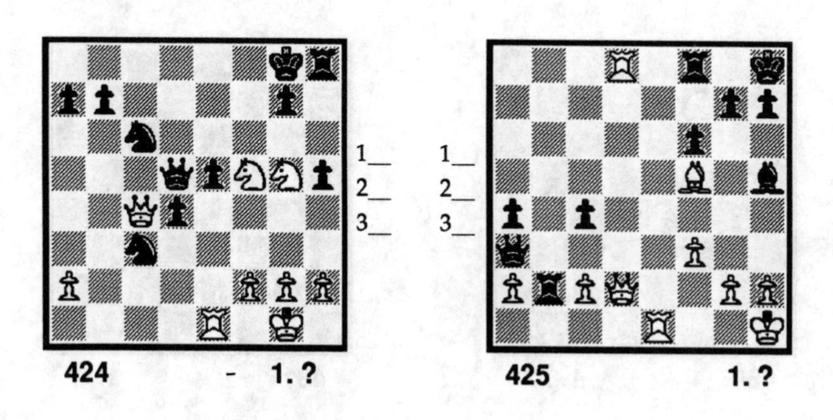

424 1. ?

425 1. ?

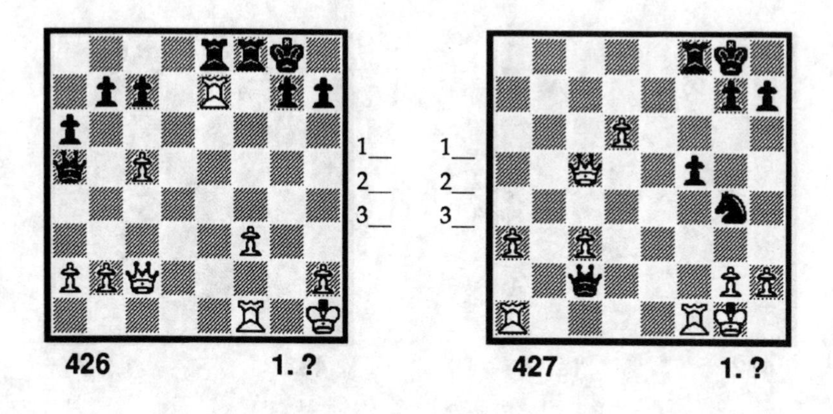

426 1. ?

427 1. ?

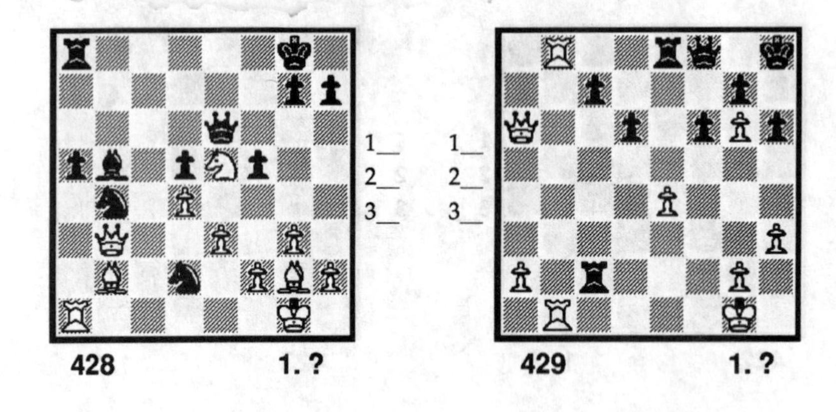

428 1. ?

429 1. ?

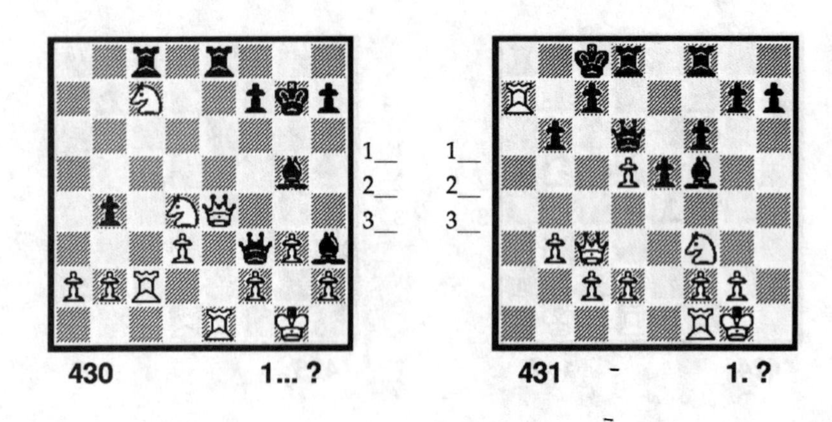

430 1... ?

431 1. ?

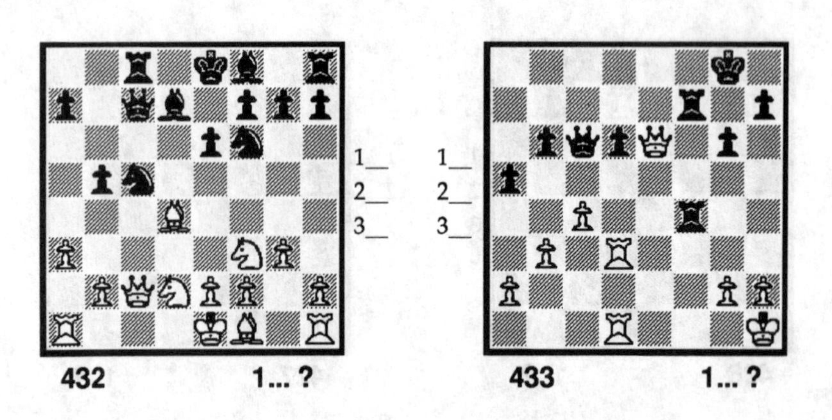

432 1... ?

433 1... ?

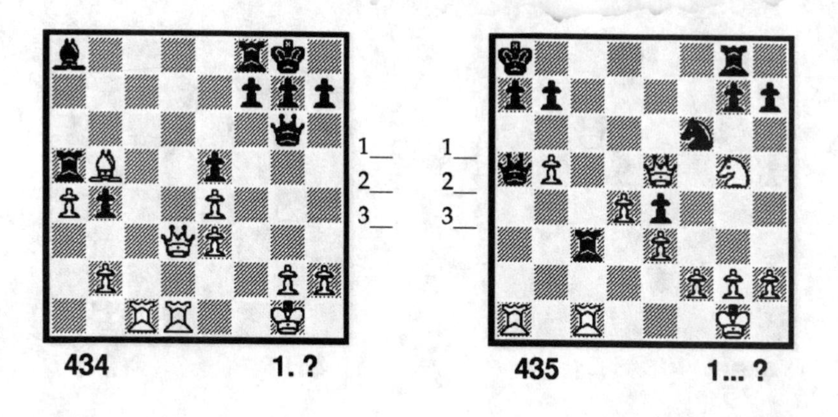

434 1. ?

435 1... ?

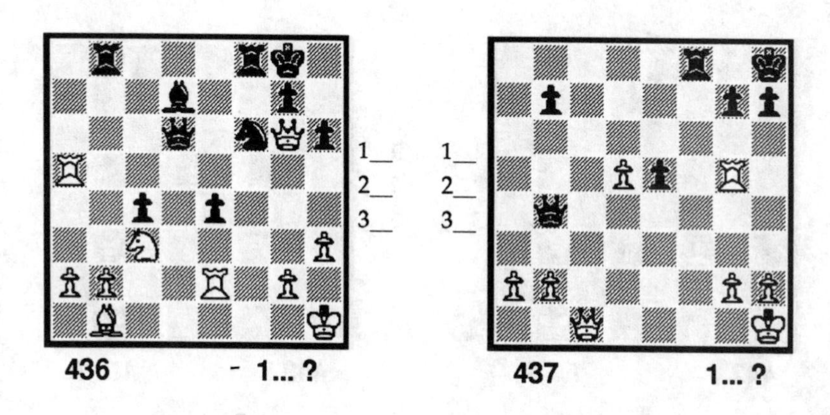

436 1... ?

437 1... ?

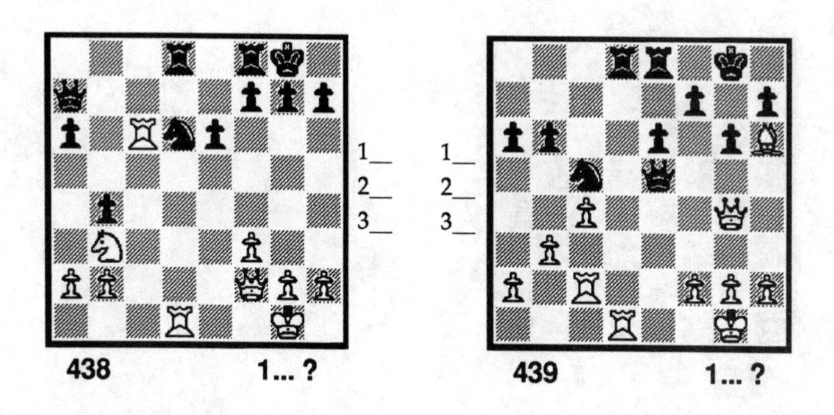

438 1... ?

439 1... ?

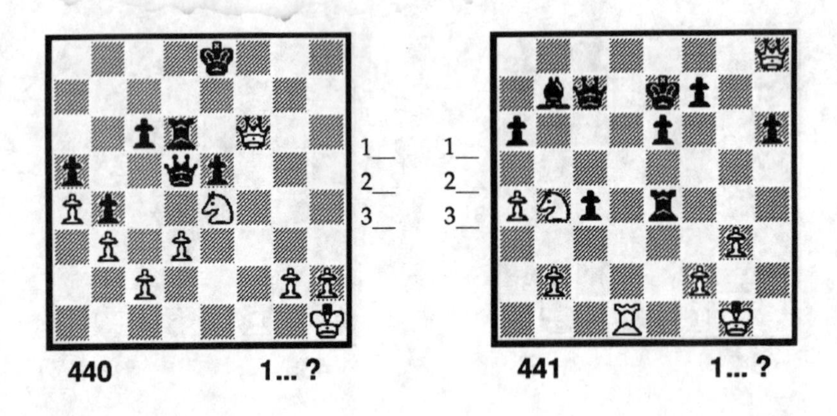

440 1... ?

441 1... ?

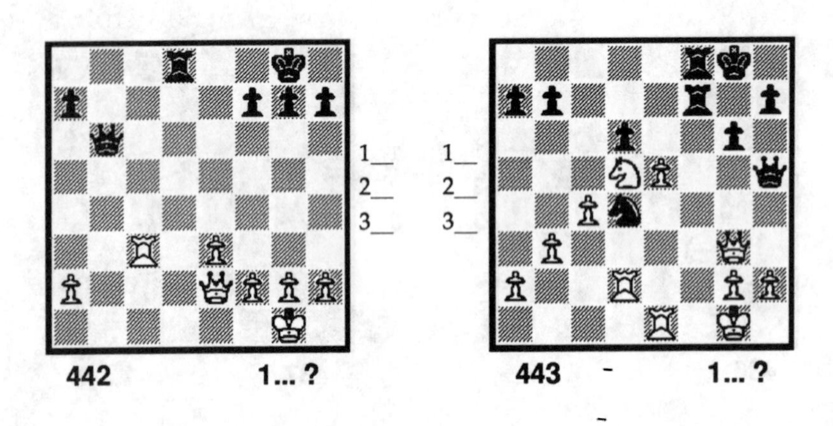

442 1... ?

443 1... ?

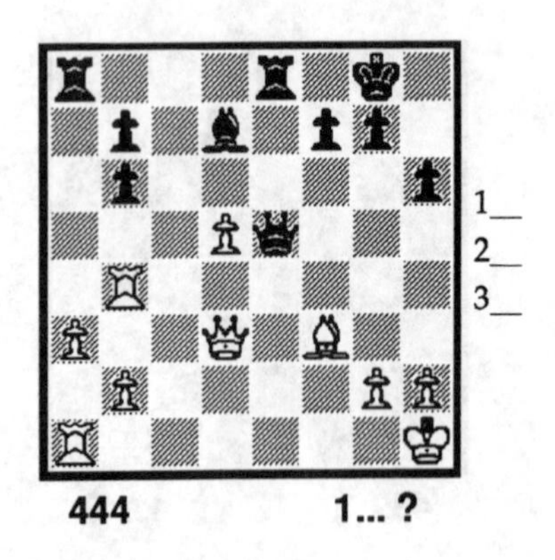

444 1... ?

CHAPTER 11

MIXED THEMES

The diagrams in this section should prove entertaining and challenging if only because of their diverse qualities. Since the student is not given a direct hint as to the nature of the motif by a definitive chapter heading, a more realistic, practical drill for over-the-board play is conveyed.

Continue to practice and review this book on a regular basis. Repetition is the key to recognizing these patterns when they occur in your games.

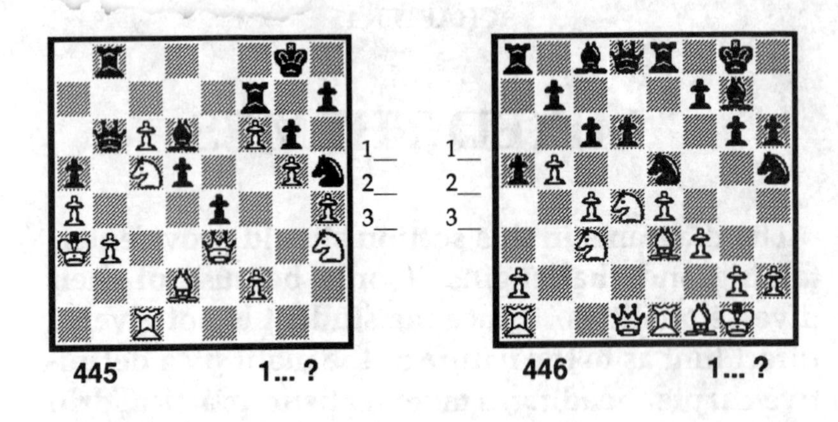

445 1... ?

446 1... ?

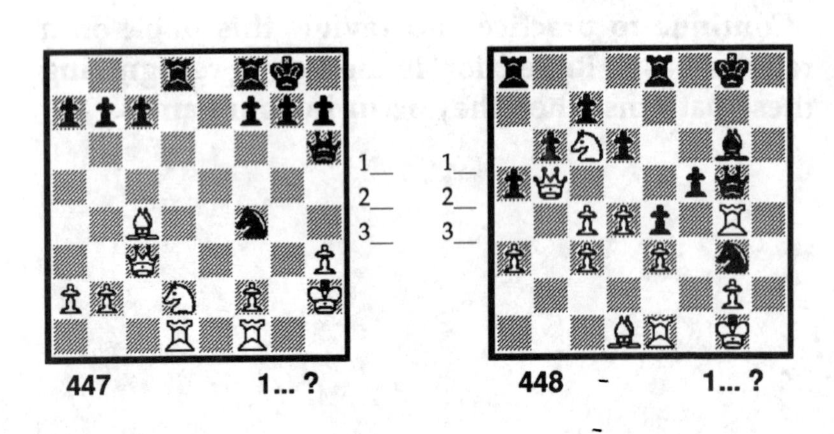

447 1... ?

448 1... ?

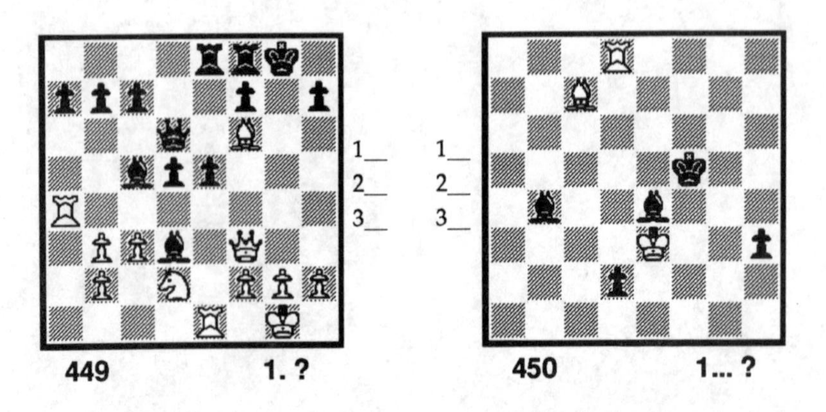

449 1. ?

450 1... ?

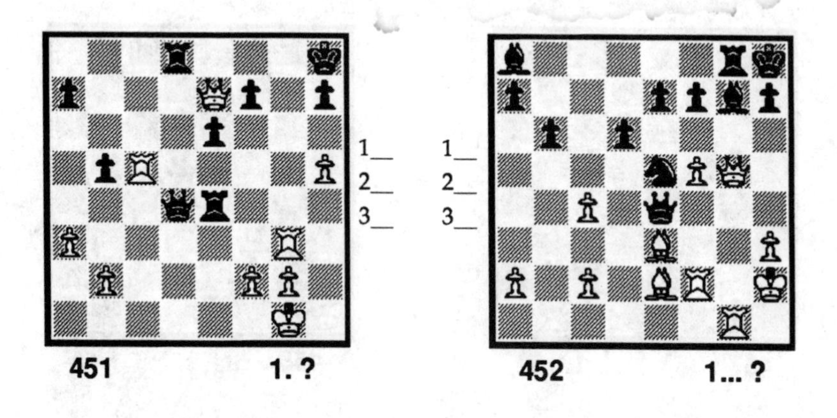

451 1. ?

452 1... ?

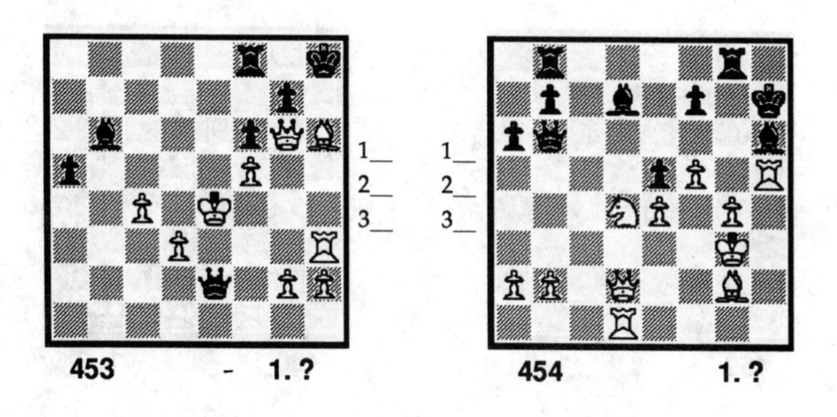

453 1. ?

454 1. ?

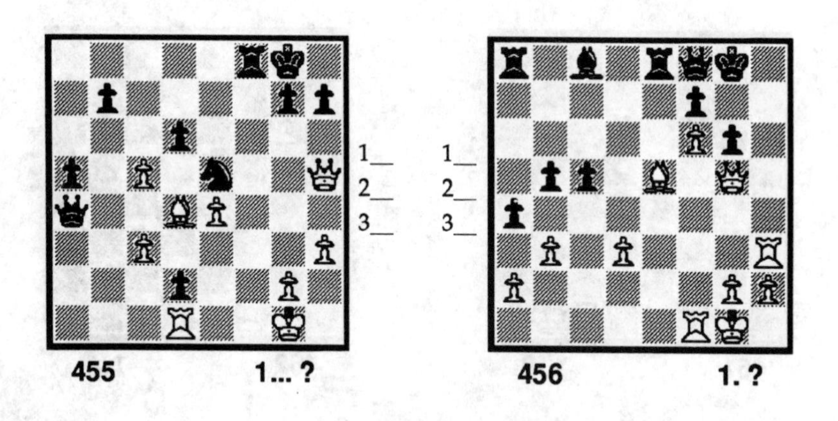

455 1... ?

456 1. ?

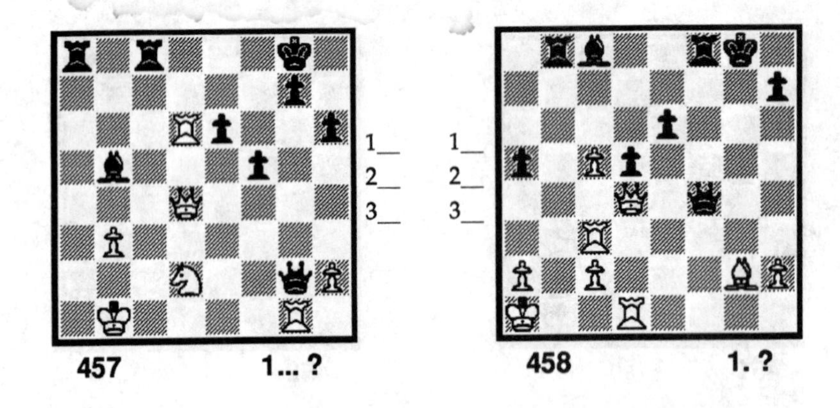

457 1... ?

458 1. ?

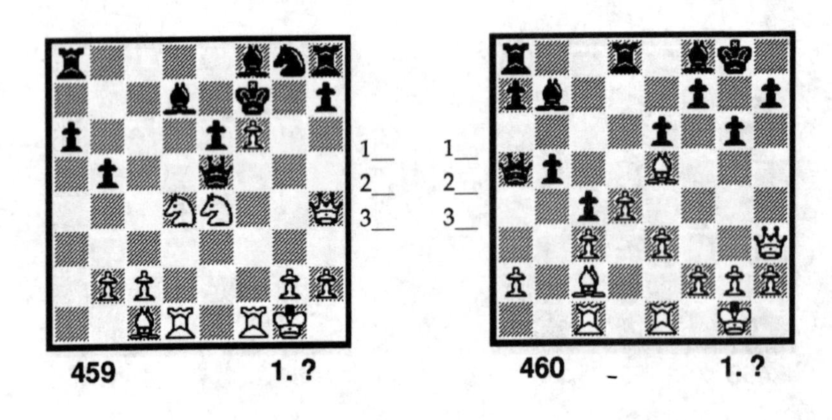

459 1. ?

460 1. ?

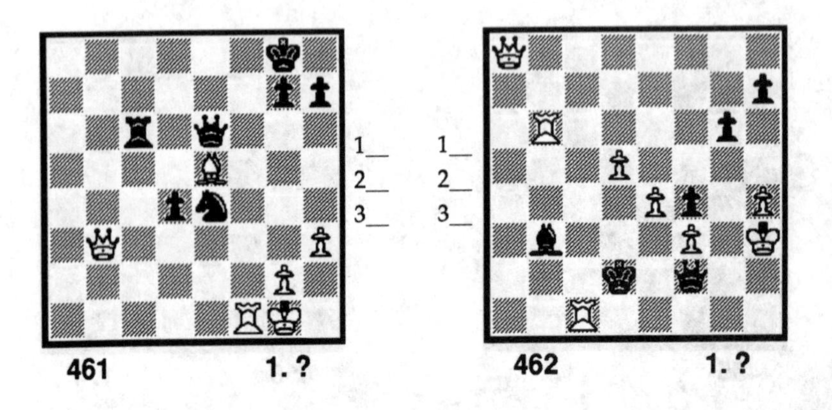

461 1. ?

462 1. ?

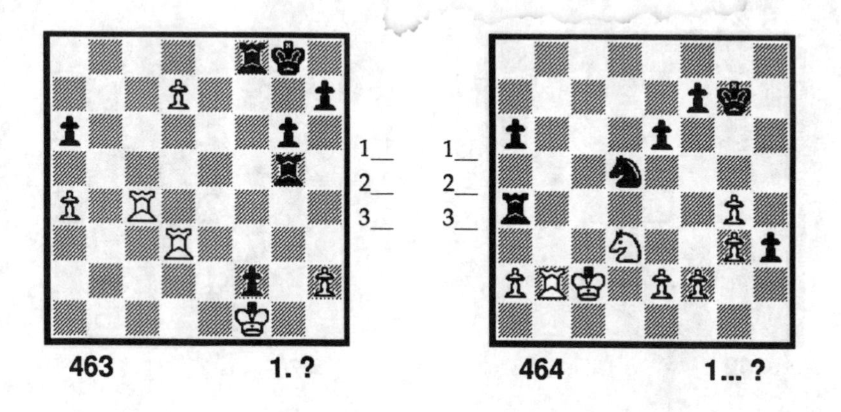
1__
2__
3__
1__
2__
3__
463
1. ?
464
1... ?

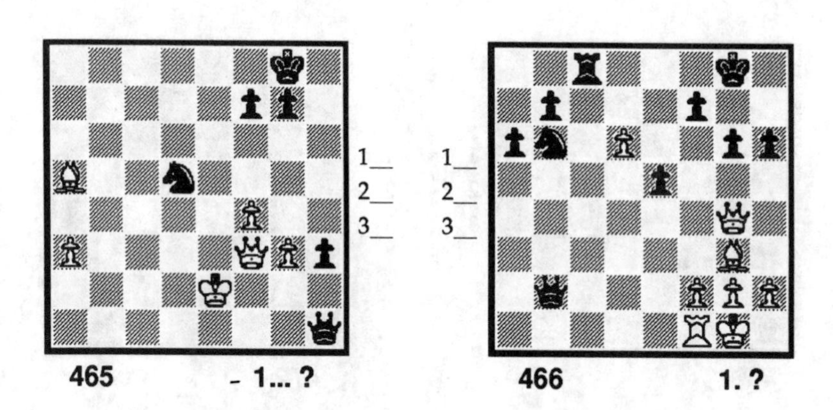
1__
2__
3__
1__
2__
3__
465
1... ?
466
1. ?

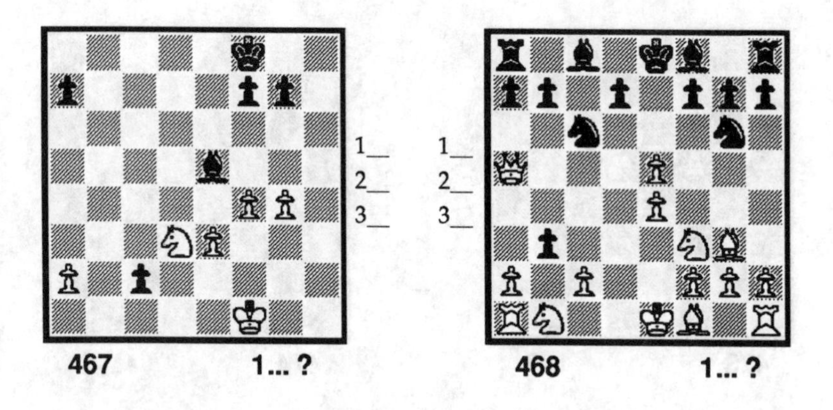
1__
2__
3__
1__
2__
3__
467
1... ?
468
1... ?

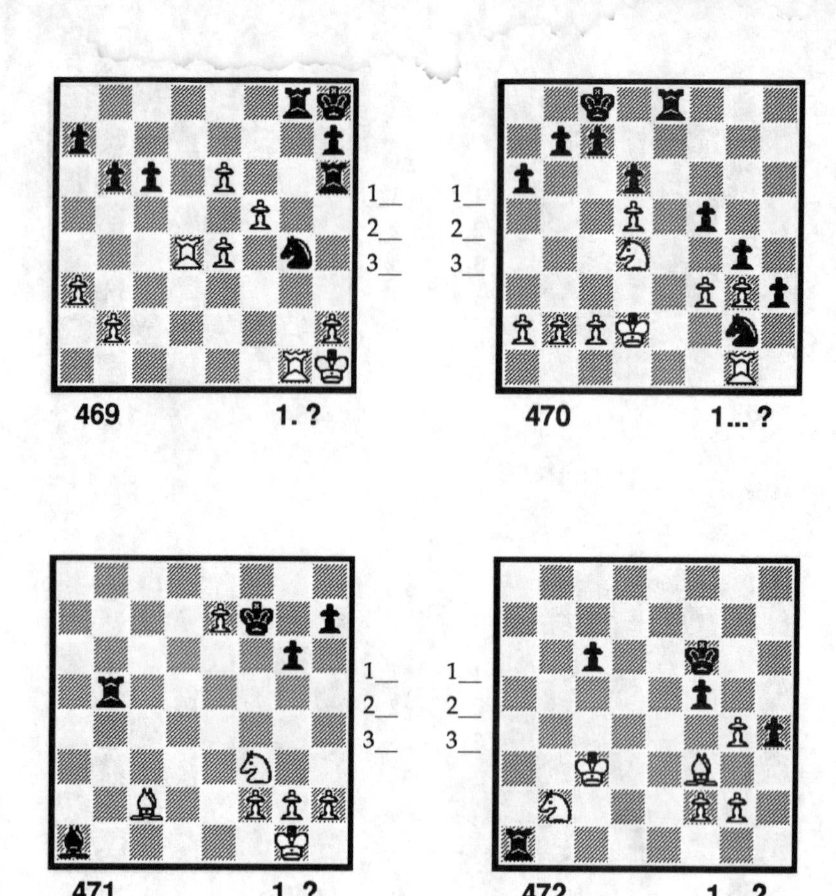
1__
2__
3__
1__
2__
3__
469
1. ?
470
1... ?
1__
2__
3__
1__
2__
3__
471
1. ?
472
1... ?

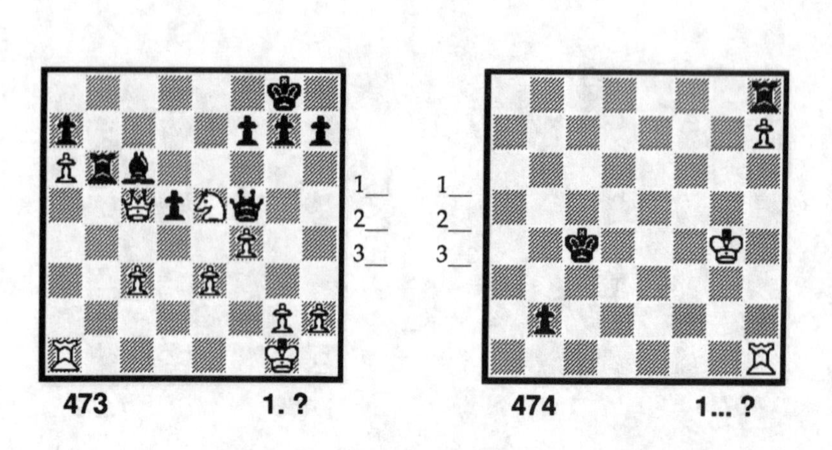
1__
2__
3__
1__
2__
3__
473
1. ?
474
1... ?

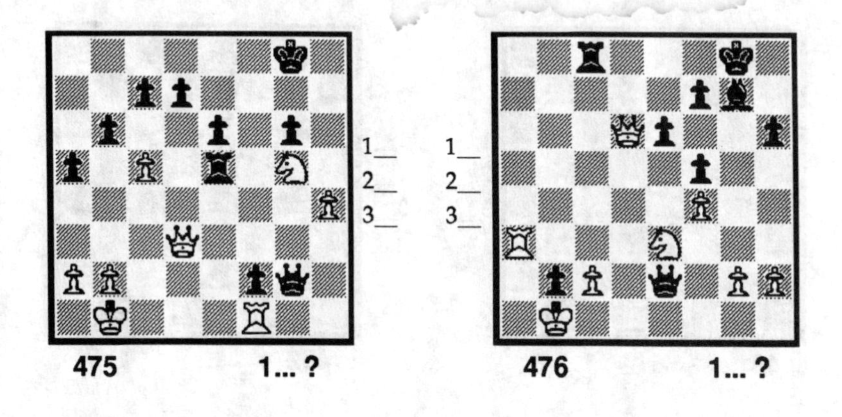

475 **1... ?**

476 **1... ?**

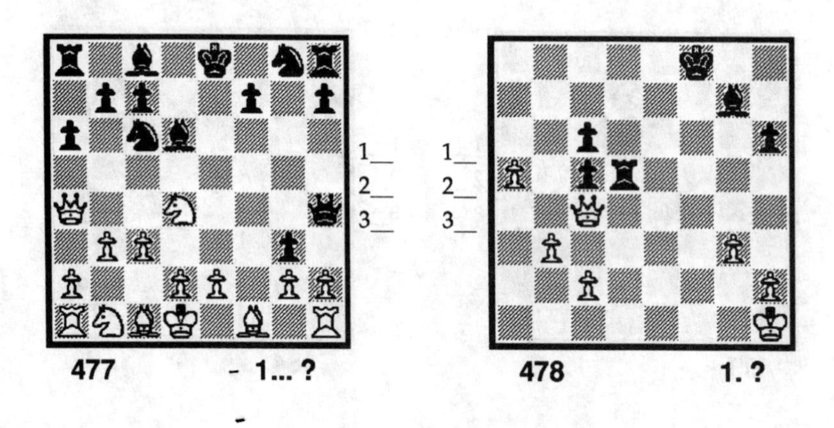

477 **1... ?**

478 **1. ?**

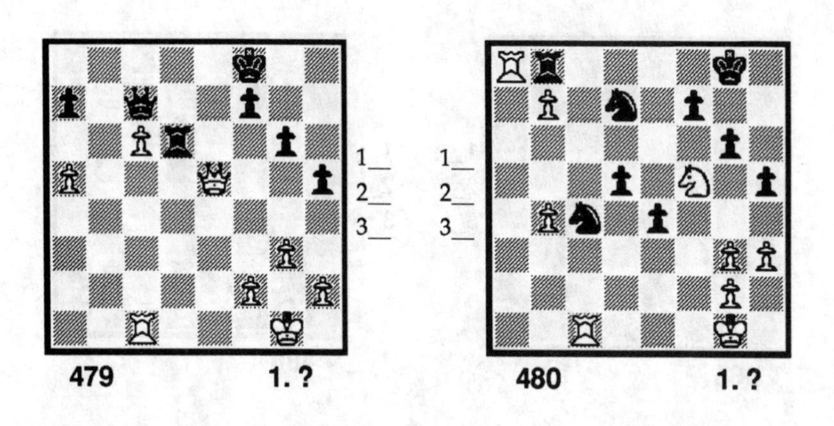

479 **1. ?**

480 **1. ?**

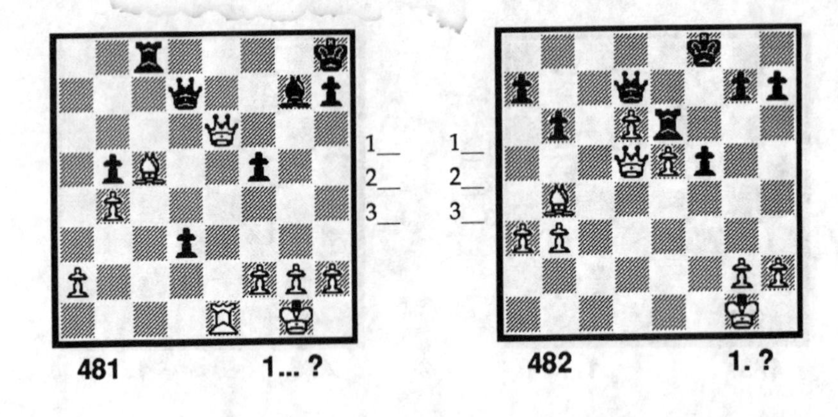

481 1... ?

482 1. ?

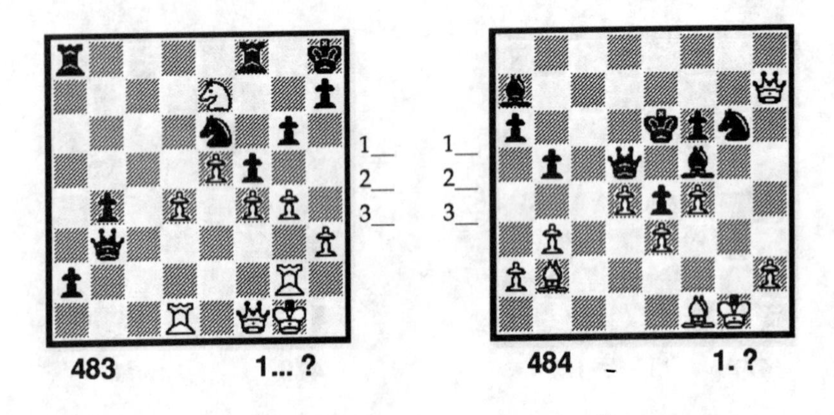

483 1... ?

484 1. ?

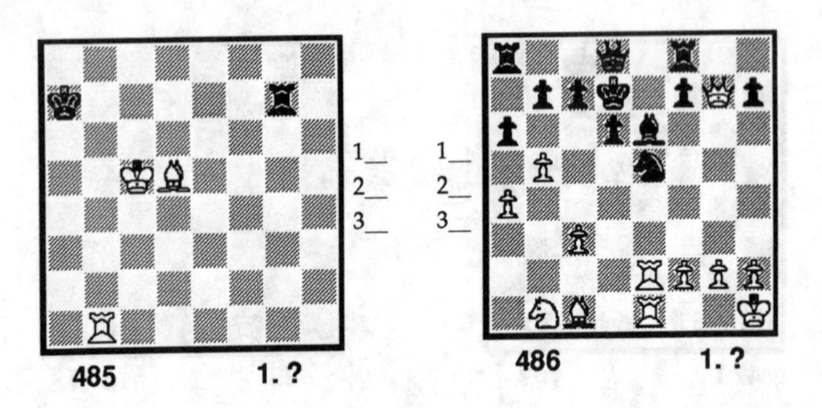

485 1. ?

486 1. ?

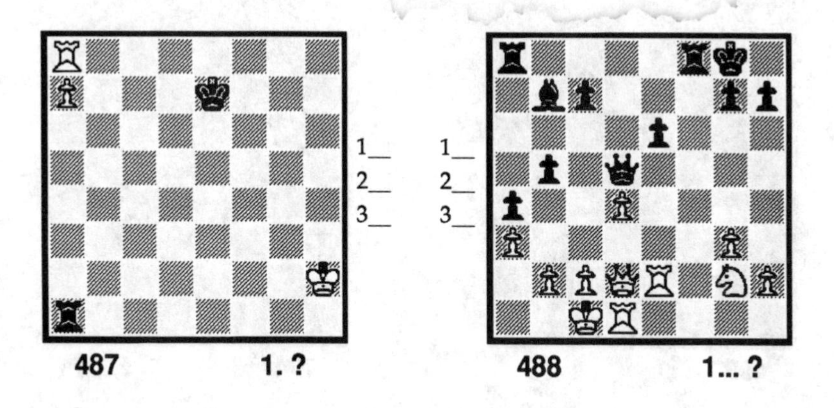

487 1. ?

488 1... ?

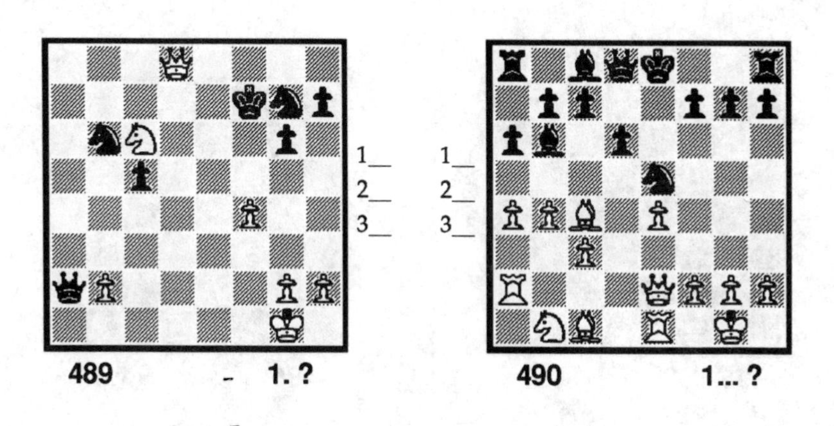

489 1. ?

490 1... ?

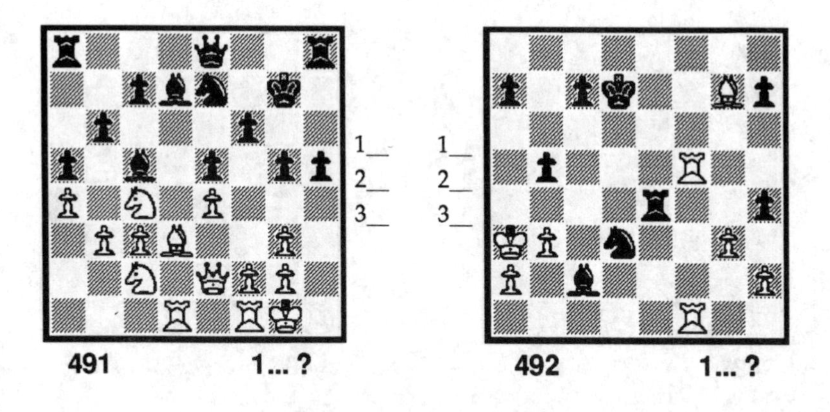

491 1... ?

492 1... ?

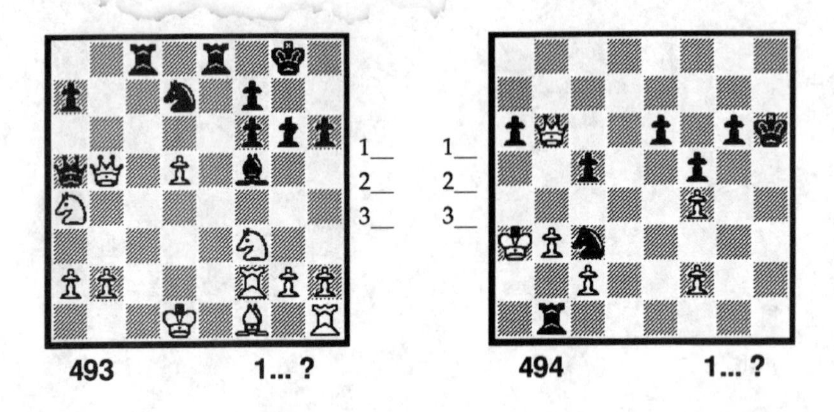

493 1... ?

494 1... ?

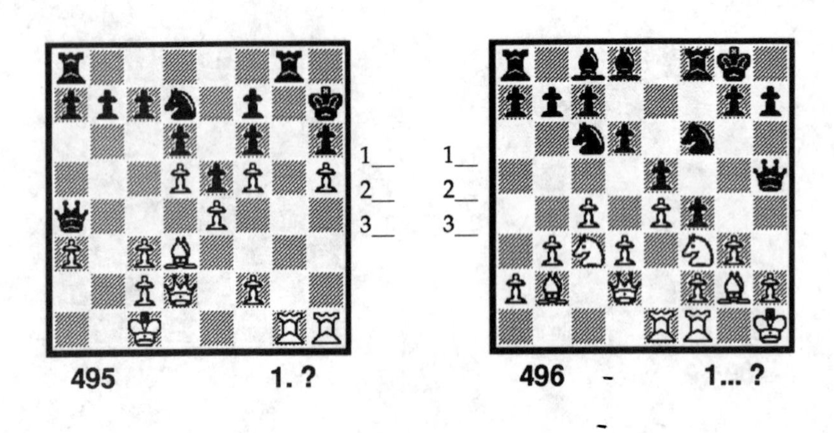

495 1. ?

496 1... ?

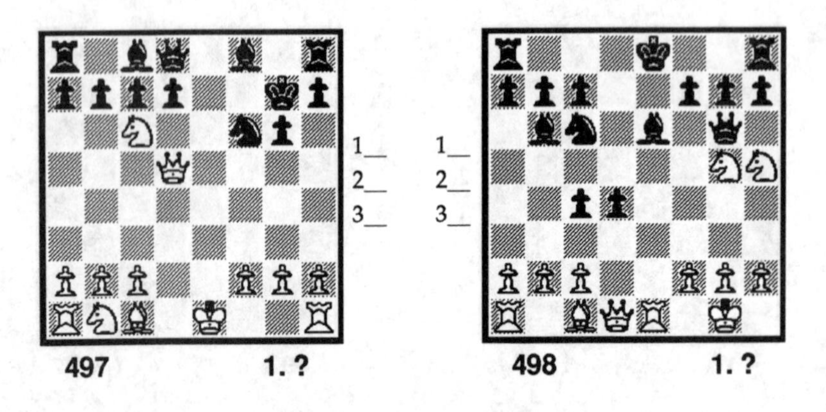

497 1. ?

498 1. ?

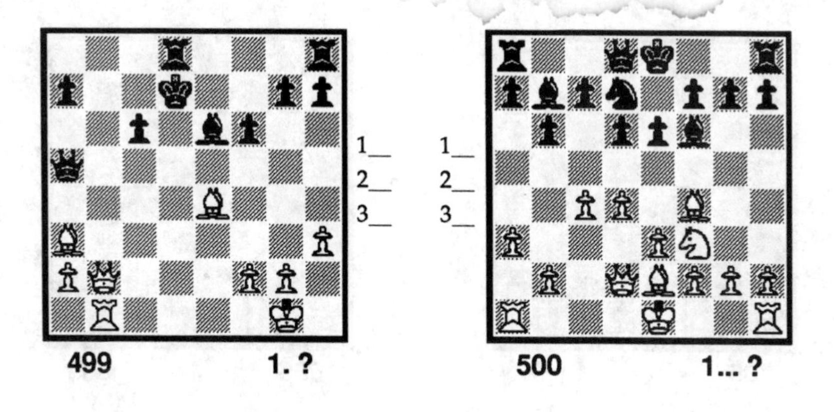

499 1. ?

500 1... ?

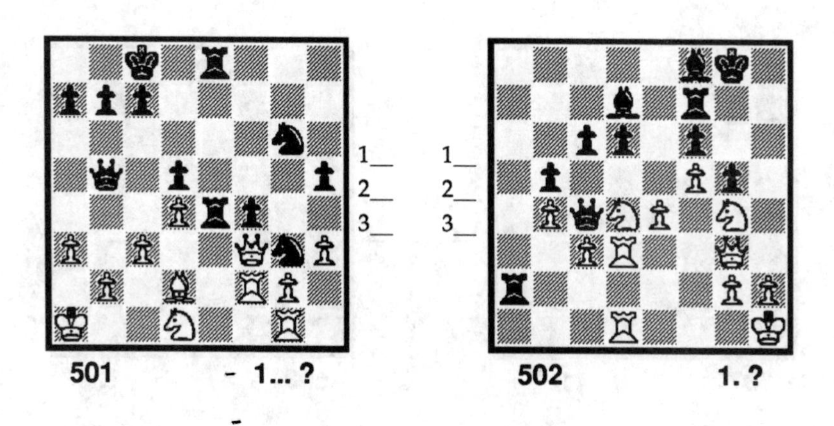

501 1... ?

502 1. ?

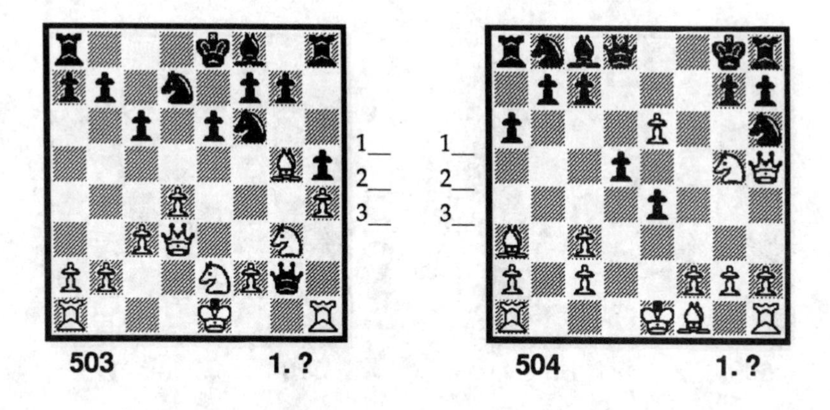

503 1. ?

504 1. ?

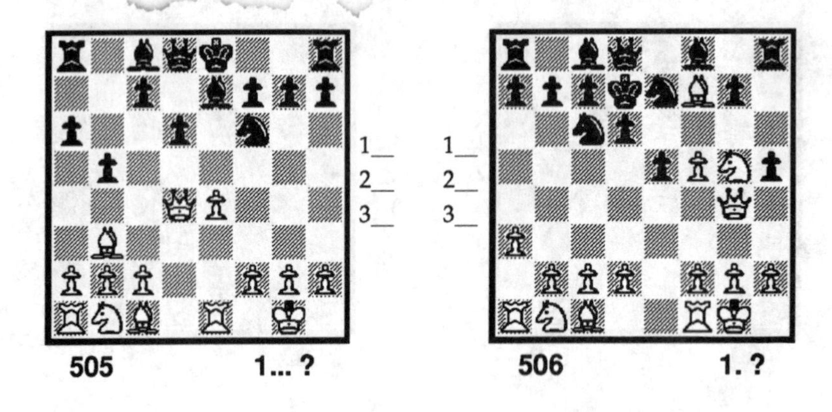
1__
2__
3__
1__
2__
3__
505
1... ?
506
1. ?

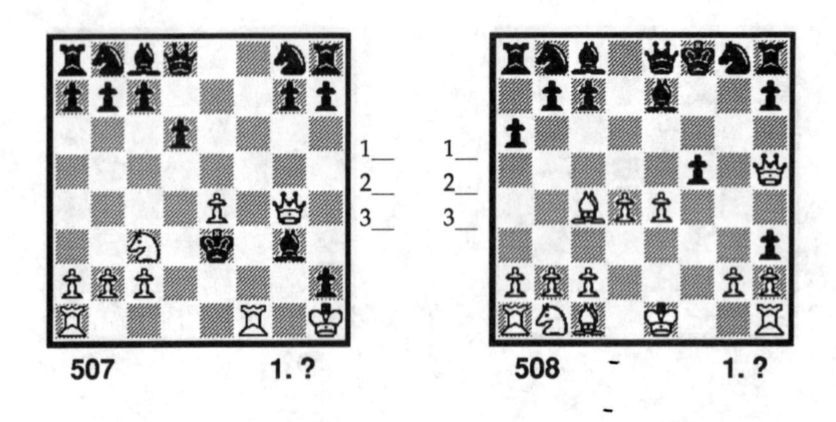
1__
2__
3__
1__
2__
3__
507
1. ?
508
1. ?

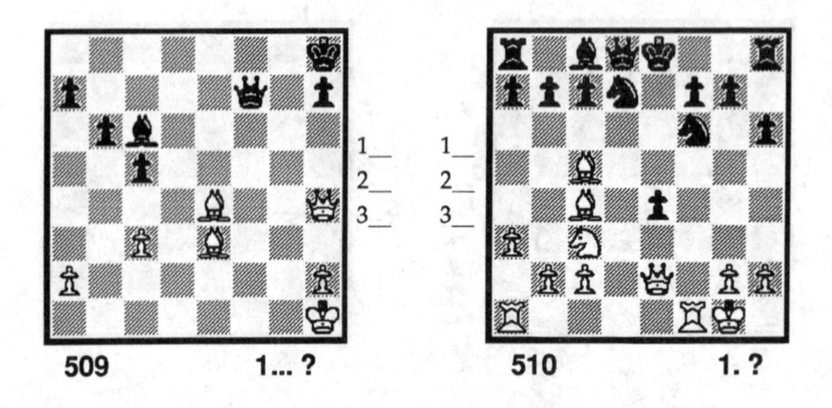
1__
2__
3__
1__
2__
3__
509
1... ?
510
1. ?

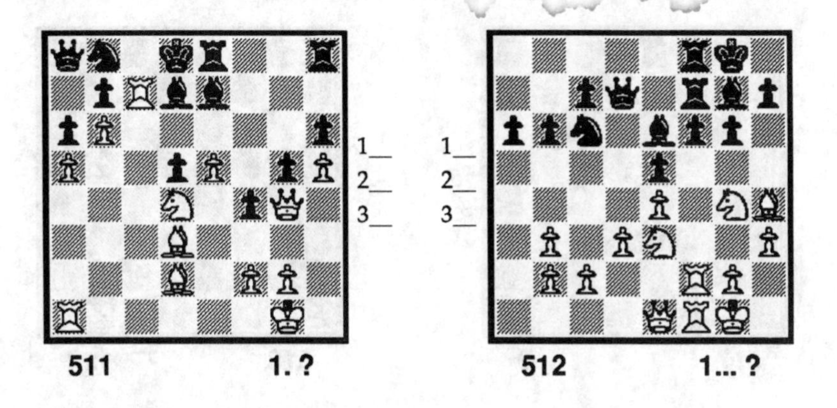
1__
2__
3__
1__
2__
3__
511
1. ?
512
1... ?

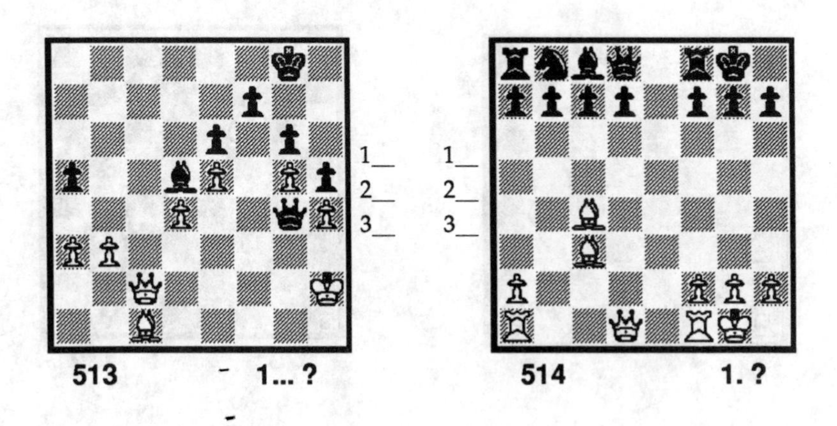
1__
2__
3__
1__
2__
3__
513
1... ?
514
1. ?

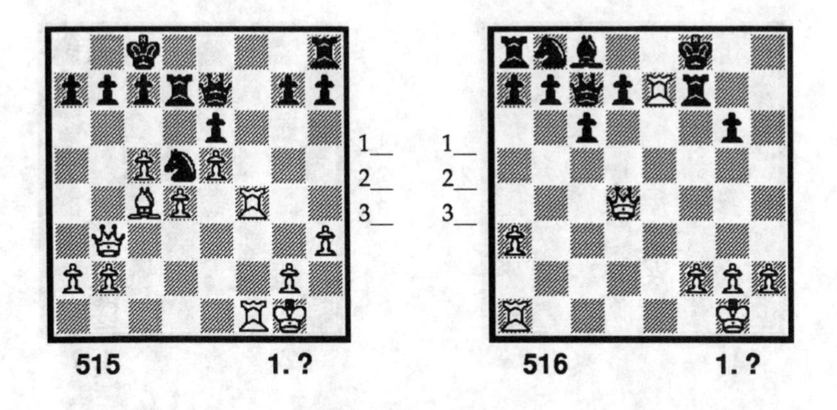
1__
2__
3__
1__
2__
3__
515
1. ?
516
1. ?

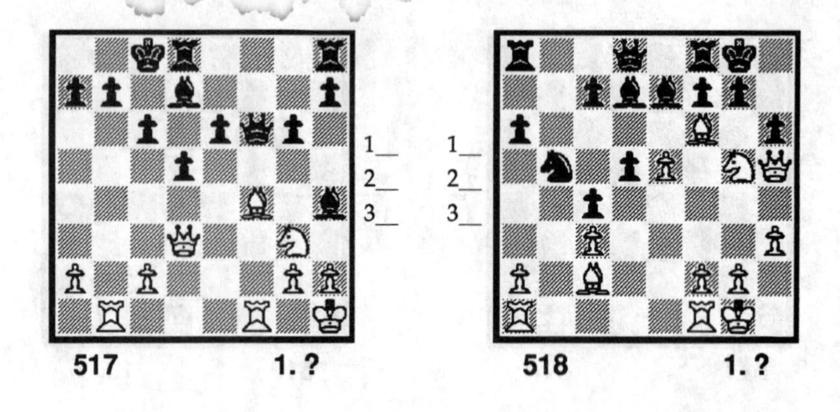

517 1. ?

518 1. ?

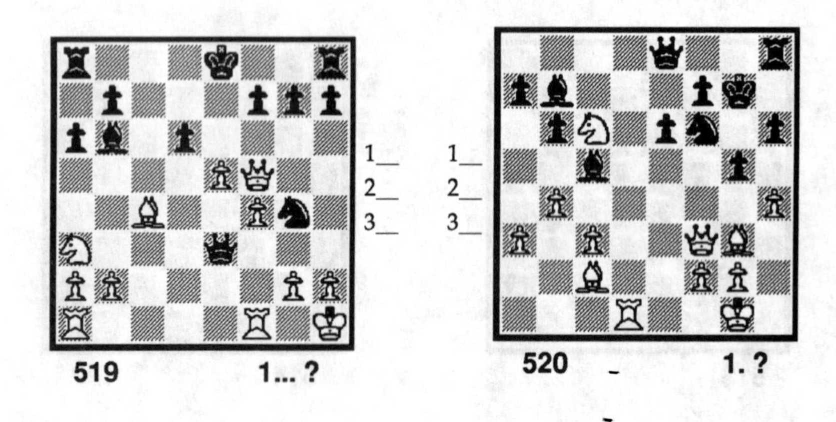

519 1... ?

520 1. ?

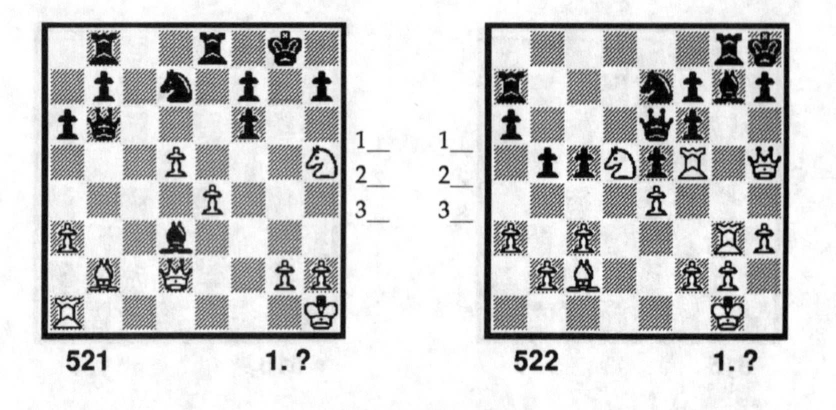

521 1. ?

522 1. ?

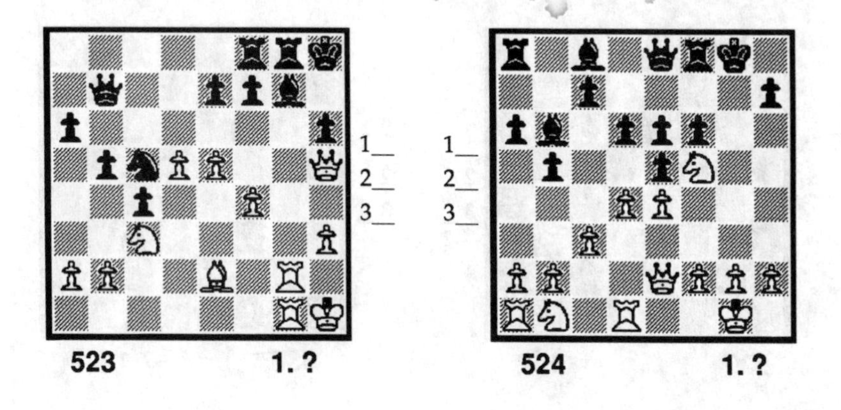

523 1. ?

524 1. ?

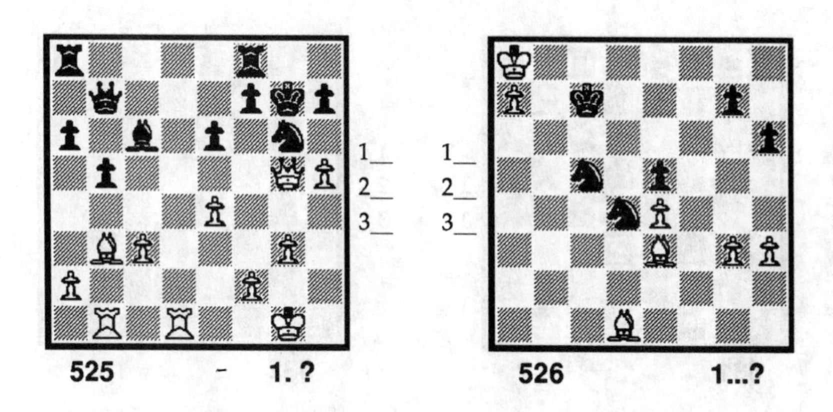

525 1. ?

526 1...?

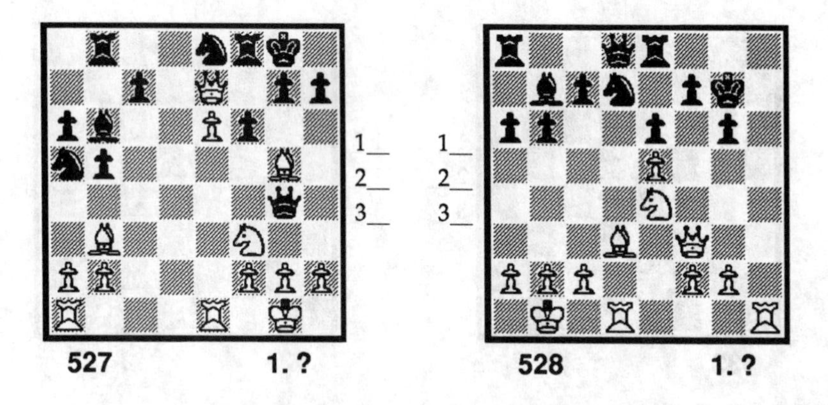

527 1. ?

528 1. ?

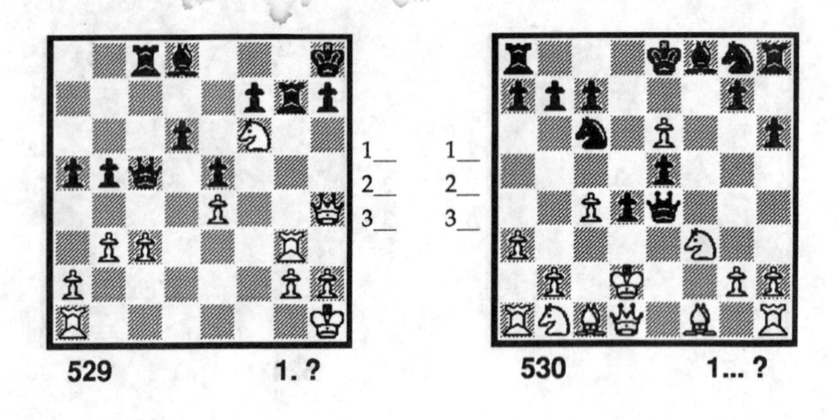

529 1. ?

1__ 2__ 3__

530 1... ?

1__ 2__ 3__

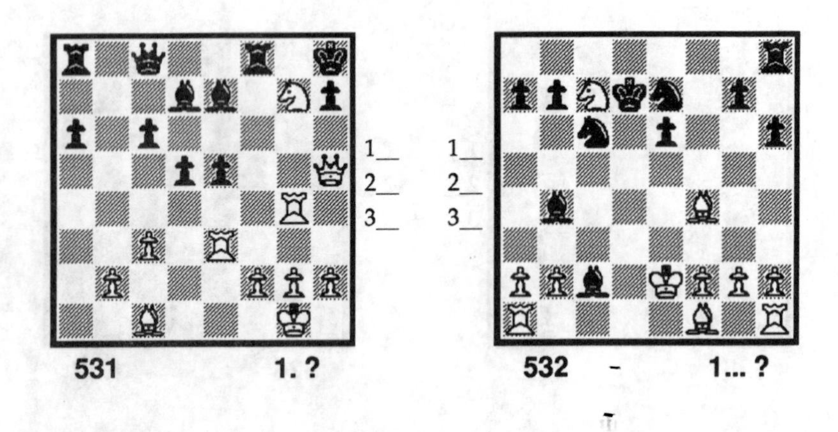

531 1. ?

1__ 2__ 3__

532 1... ?

1__ 2__ 3__

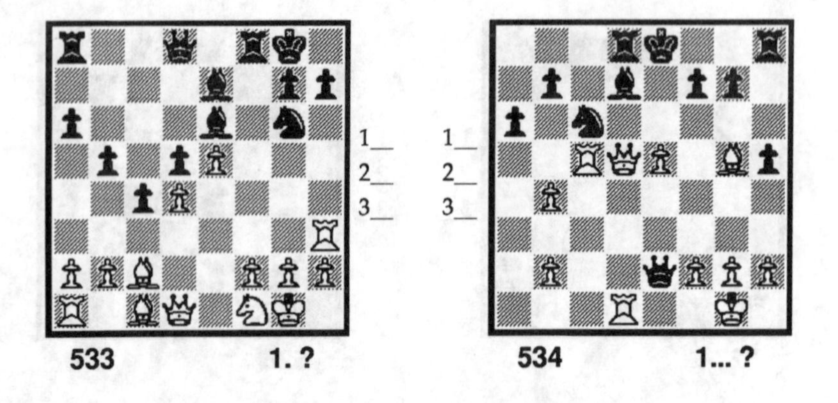

533 1. ?

1__ 2__ 3__

534 1... ?

1__ 2__ 3__

SOLUTIONS

CHAPTER 1
DISCOVERY

01) 1.Qh6+! Bxh6 2.Ng5+ Kh8 3.Rh7#.

02) 1...Qg2+!! 2.Kxg2 Nf4+ 3. Kg1 Nh3#.

03) 1...Rxf3! 2.Qxe2 Rxf1#.

04) 1...Qxd4 2.exd4 Bb4+ 3.Kd1 Re1#.

05) 1...Qg2+! 2.Kxg2 Rxg3+ and mate.

06) 1...Nf3#.

07) 1...Bd3+ 2.Ke1 Rf1#.

08) 1...Ng5! and wins (2.Qxg6 Nxf3+ 3.Bxf3 hxg6).

09) 1. Bd6+ Kxd6 2.Rd3 wins the Queen.

10) 1.Qd8+!! Kxd8 2.Bg5+-+ Ke8 3.Rd8#.

11) 1.Qd8+ Kxd8 2.Bg5+ Ke8 3.Rd8#.

12) 1...Rd1!! and Black wins. (2.Qxc6 Rxe1#, or 2.Rxd1 Qxf3).

13) 1.Rh8+! Kxh8 2.Bxg7+ wins the Black Queen.

14) 1...Qxb1+ 2.Nxb1 Ba6! and wins.

15) 1...Be4+!! wins. (2.Ka1 Qxa2+! 3.Rxa2 Rxa2#, or 2.fxe4 bxa2+ 3.Ka1 Qxg3).

16) 1.Qe6+ Kh7 (or 1...Kh5) **2.Nf6+ gxf6 3.Qxe1.**

17) 1.Bd5!! (now, if 1...Qxd5 2.Rxf8+ mates, or 1...Rxd5 2.Rxf8#. Finally 1...Rxf2 2.Qg8#).

18) 1.Nxc7 Qxc7 2.Bxe6+ and 3.Qxc7.

19) 1.f3 Bh5 2.f4! winning a piece after 2...Bxe2 3.fxg5 Qxg5 4.Rxe2 or 2...exf4 3.Bxh5.

20) 1...Nf3+ 2.gxf3 Qg6+ 3.Kh1 Ng3+ picking up the White Queen.

21) 1.Ng5 Qxg5 2.Bxb7.

22) 1.Nxd7 and wins, since 1...Rxe2 is met by 2.Nxf6+ and 1...Rxd7 fails to 2.Qxe8.

23) 1.Nxc6 Qxc3 (1...Qxc6 2.Qg7#) **2.Nxe7+ Kh8 3.Nf7#.**

24) 1.Qxf8! Qxf8 2.c8=Q+ and wins.

25) 1.Be7! Re8 2.Bb4 threatening both the Queen and mate at e8.

26) 1.Ne6!! Qxe3 2.Nd5! Qe4 3.Ndc7#.

27) 1.Nxe5! Bxd1 2.Bxf7+ Ke7 3.Nd5#.

28) 1.d5! and wins the Nb6.

29) 1.Nf6!! winning, as 1...Nxd3 is met by 2.Rxh7#, or 1...gxf6 allows 2.Qxh7#, or 1...h6 2.Qh7#.

30) 1.Qd8+! Kxd8 2.Ba5+ Ke8 3.Rd8#.

31) 1...Qxg3 2.fxg3 Rd8+ and 3...Rxc8.

32) 1...Qxg2+ 2.Kxg2 Nf5+ and 3...Nxh6.

Ng3+! 2.hxg3 hxg3+ 3.Bxh5 Qh4#.

.Bf8+! Bh5 2.Qxh5+ gxh5 3.Rh6#.

) 1.Qxg8+! Ke7 (1...Kxg8 2.Nf6#!) **2.Nd6 Rxd8 3.Qxf7#.**

36) 1.Rxh6+ Kxh6 2.Nxd5+ and **3.Nxe7.**

37) 1.Rxd6! Qxd6 2.Bxg7+ Kg8 3.c5+ and wins the Queen.

38) 1.Nc5+ wins the Black Queen.

39) 1.Rh8+ Kxh8 2.e6+ Qg7 3.Bxg7+

40) 1...Bxd4! 2.Rxh5 e2+ 3.Kh1 e1=Q#.

41) 1.Bh5+ g6 2.Nxg6 Nb6 (2...hxg6 3.Bxg6#) **3.Ne5#.**

42) 1.Qd5 Qc1+ 2.Rf1+.

43) 1.Rh1 Kh5 2.Kg3+ and wins the Bishop.

44) 1...Nh4+ 2.Ke1 (or 2.Kg1 Qg4#) **2...Nxf3#.**

45) 1. Nf6+! Kxf6 2.Nh5+ Kf7 3.Qh7#.

46) 1...Bxf5! winning a piece. If 2.Bxf5 Rxg3+! 3. fxg3 (3.K moves 3...Qxh4+ mates) 3...d3+ wins the Queen.

47) 1.Qg8+!! and wins. 1...Kxg8 2.Be6+ Kh8 3.Rg8#.

48) 1.Bh7+ Kh8 2.Bg8+! Kxg8 (2...Bh6 3.Qh7#) **3.Qh7#.**

49) 1.Qxd8+! Kxd8 2.Bc2+ and 3.Bxa4.

50) 1...Ng3! 2.Qxg6 Nde2#.

51) 1...Rxf1+! 2.Kxf1 Bd3+ and 3...Qxf4.

52) 1.Rxf6! gxf6 2.Qxd7+! Kxd7 3.dxc5+ followed by cxb6.

53) 1...d3! 2.Bxf6 (2.Qxd3 Qxb2) **2...dxe2.**

54) 1...Nxf2! 2.Kxf2 Bxg3+ and 3...Qxd1.

55) 1.Nf7! Qf6 (1...Kxf7 2.fxg5+ winning the Queen) **2.fxg5** winning material.

56) 1...Bxd3! 2.Qxd3 Bxh2+ 3.Nxh2 Rxd3.

57) 1...Ne3! 2.Re1 Nc4+ 3.Bxc4 Rxe1.

58) 1.Nd6 Re7 (or 1...Rg8 2.Nf7#) **2.Nxc8 Rxc8 3.Bxe7.**

59) 1...Nxd4 2.Qxd4 Ng4+ and 3...Bxd4.

60) 1...Nc7! attacking both the Bb5 and Ne5.

61) 1.Ng5! and wins. If 1...Nxg5 2.Qg7#.

62) 1.Rxe5! Qxe5 2.Ng6! and now on 2...Qxh2 3.Nde7#!

63) 1...Rxe2 2.Qxe2 Qc3+ 3.Qc2 Qxc2#.

64) 1...Be3!! and wins, since white cannot defend the Bf2 and the threat of Qxg2# simultaneously.

CHAPTER 2

QUEEN SACRIFICE

65) 1...Ng4! threatening 2...Qxh2#, and if 2.Qxh3 then 2...Nf2#.

66) 1...Qf1! 2.Rxf1 Rxf1#.

67) 1...Qh3!! forces mate since 2.gxh3 allows 2...Nxh3#.

68) 1...Qg1+! 2.Kxg1 Nxe2+ and wins.

69) 1...Qh1+!! 2.Kxh1 Bf3+ 3.Kg1 Rd1#.

70) 1.Rh8+ Kf7 2.Qxg7+! Kxg7 3.R(h1)h7#.

71) 1.Qg6+!! Bxg6 2.Ng5+! hxg5 3.hxg6#.

72) 1.Qxd7! Rxd7 2.Re8+ Kh7 3.Rcc8 and wins.

73) 1.Qg6!! fxg6 (if 1...hxg6 then 2.Rh3# or 1...Rg8 2.Qxh7+! Kxh7 3.Rh3#) **2.Nxg6+ hxg6 3.Rh3#.**

74) 1.Qxh7+! Kxh7 2.Rh1+ Bh3 3.Rxh3#.

75) 1.Qf7+! Rxf7 2.exf7#.

76) 1.Qxh7+! Kxh7 2.hxg5+ Kg6 (2...Kg8 3.Ne7#) **3.Ne7#.**

77) 1...Qxf1+! 2.Kxf1 Bd3+-+ 3.Ke1 Rf1#.

78) 1.Qxh7+! Kxh7 2.Rh3+ Kg8 3.Rh8#.

79) 1.Qxf8+ Qxf8 2.Rxh7#.

80) 1.Bg7+! Kf7 2.Qe6+! Nxe6 3.dxe6#.

81) 1.Qxg6!! hxg6 2.Rf3 and 3.Rh3 will be mate.

82) 1...Qd3+!! 2.Kxd3 (2.Ke1 Qxb1) **2...Bxc6+** followed by 3...Bxa4.

83) 1.Qe8+! Kxe8 2.Nf6+ Kd8 3.Nf7#.

84) 1.Qxh7+! Kxh7 2.Rh4+ Kg8 3.Re8#.

85) 1.Qxc6+! bxc6 2.Ba6#.

86) 1.Qxf4! Bxf4 2.Rxh5 gxh5 3.Rxh5 and mate by Rh8.

87) 1.Bh6! and now if either 1...Qxg4 or 1...Rxg4, then 2.Rf8 is checkmate.

88) 1.Qxc6+! bxc6 (1...Kb8 2.Nd7+ forces Black to give up the Queen) **2.Ba6+ Kb8 3.Nxc6#.**

89) 1.Qh6! gxh6 (1...gxf6 2.Nxf6+ Kh8 3.Qxh7#) **2.Nxh6#.**

90) 1.Rxd4 f4 (on 1...exd4 2.Bxd4! Qxd4 3.Nxf5+ and wins) **2.Rxf4!** winning.

91) 1...Qa4!! 2.Bd3 (2.Nxa4 Na2#) **2...Bxd3** and wins.

92) 1.Qxf6! gxf6 (1...Qxe4 2.Qxf7+!) **2.Rg4+** winning a piece.

93) 1.Qxh6+! gxh6 2.Bf6#.

CHAPTER 3
THE PIN

94) 1...Rxc5 2.Qc5 Rc8! and if 3.Qxb6, Rxc1+ followed by 4.axb6 winning a whole Rook.

95) 1.Rb1! and Black Resigns, for if 1...Qxc5 2.Rxb7#.

96) 1...Bg5! 2.f4 Bxf4! and White Resigns, as 3.Qxf4 is met with 3...Qxb2#.

97) 1...Qxg3! 2. Kxg3 gxf6 White resigns.

98) 1...Bxf2+! 2.Kf1 (on 2.Kxf2, Qxe5 wins the Queen since the Nf3 is pinned) **2...Bxe1** and wins.

99) 1...Bxg2! 2.Rxe8 (or 2.Qxg2 Rxe2) **2...Bc6+!** winning an important pawn.

100) 1...Re1! 2.Qxe1 Nxf3+ 3.Rxf3 Qxe1+.

101) 1.Bh7+ Kxh7 2.g8=Q+! Kxg8 3.Qxh2.

102) 1...Rxe2+! 2.Kd1 (2.Nxe2 drops the Queen) **2...Rxd2+! 3.Kxd2 Ne4+** and wins.

103) 1...Nc3 wins since 2.Nxc3 Rxe1 wins the exchange, while 2.Bf3 allows 2...Qxh3.

104) 1...Ne4! (the "relative" pin is broken) **2.Be3** (after 2.Bxd8 Black has 2...Bxf2#) **2...Bxe3 3.fxe3 Qh4+ 4.g3 Nxg3** winning easily.

105) 1...Rd8! 2.Qxf5 Rxd1#.

106) 1...Qxg2+! 2.Qxg2 Rxe2 wins the exchange.

107) 1.Ng6! and wins the Black Queen.

108) 1.Rxd3!! cxd3 2.Ne6+! fxe6 3.Rc7+ and wins Black's Queen.

109) 1.Rdxd7+ Rxd7 2.Qb5! wins.

110) 1.Qxh7+! Kxh7 2.Rh5#.

111) 1.Bc4!

112) 1.Bd4 Qxd4 (1...e5 2.Bxe5) **2.Qh6#.**

113) 1.Qf6#.

114) 1...Rc2! 2.Bxc2 (or 2.Qe3 Ne2+ 3.Kf2 Ng4+ winning) **2...Ne2#.**

115) 1.Bxd5! Bxd5 (not 1...cxd5 2.Rxa6) **2.Qxf6+** followed by 3.Qxe7.

116) 1.f6! Bg4 (if 1...gxf6 then 2.Qg6+ Kh8 3.Qh7#) **2.Qg6!** and mate next.

117) 1...Rxf3 2.Qxf2 Rfxh3+ 3.Kg1 Rh1#.

118) 1.Bc5! Kf8 2.Qf6! winning the Bishop since 2...Bxc5 allows 3.Qxf7#.

119) 1.c6! Rxh6! (a nice try... now if 2.Rxh6 it's stalemate) **2.c7! Rc6 3.Rh6 Rxh6 4.c8=B#.**

120) 1.f6! (threatening 2.Qh7#) **1...hxg5 2.Qg6!** and wins.

121) 1.Ne7+! Qxe7 2.Qxc8+ Qf8 3.Bh7+! wins the Queen.

122) 1.Nxe5! dxe5 2.Qd8#.

123) 1.Nxe6! Nxe6 2.Qg4! Qc6 3.Qxg7+.

124) 1.Nc7! Qxc7 2.Qxb5 wins the exchange.

125) 1.Be7! Qxg4 2.Rxd8#.

126) 1.g4+! Kxg4 2.Be6.

127) 1.Rd1! Qxc4 2.Rxd8+ K moves 3.bxc4 wins a Rook.

128) 1.c4! Ne7 (1...Nxc4 2.Rxd5) **2.c5** winning a piece.

129) 1.Bxe5 Qxe5 2.Qxe5 dxe5 3.Bxe6.

130) 1.Rxf4! exf4 2.Bh8!! and 3.Qg7# cannot be prevented.

131) 1.Qh4+! Kg8 2.Qg3+ Kh8 3.Bc3 wins the Queen.

132) 1...Qe7! and wins the Ne4 since 2.Ng3 allows 2...fxg3+.

133) 1.Nxd7 Rxd7 2.Bxd5! Rxd5 3.b6 wins a piece.

134) 1...Rxd2! 2.Qxd2 Nxe4 (Threatening 3...Ng3# and 3...Nxd2) **3.Qg2 Nf2#.**

135) 1...Bg4 2.Qxg4 Nxf2+.

136) 1.Rxg7+!! Kxg7 (or 1...Qxg7 2.Rg1) **2.Rg1** winning.

137) 1...h4! 2.Nf1 (or 2.Nh1) **2...h3** and wins the Bishop.

138) 1...Nxc3! 2.bxc3 Rxc3+! 3.Qxc3 Rxb1#.

139) 1.Be4! Qxb7 2.Bxb7 wins material.

140) 1...Qxd7! 2.Nxd7 Bxc4.

141) 1.Qa8! retains the extra piece after 1...Qxc6 2.Qxb8+.

142) 1.Ne7+! Qxe7 2.Rxe7 and now 2...Rxh6 loses to 3.Re8#.

143) 1.Nc6 Qd7 2.Ne7+! Qxe7 3.Qxd5 wins the Exchange.

144) 1...Rg4! (threatening simply 2...Bxf3+) **2.Bxg4 Qxf1#.**

145) 1.Rxh6! gxh6 2.Rg1.

146) 1.Bf4! wins the pinned Nb8.

147) 1.Rg4! wins the Queen as 1...Qxg4 allows 2.Qxf7+ and 3.Qxh7#.

CHAPTER 4
KNIGHT FORK

148) 1.Qg7+! Qxg7 2.fxg7+ Kg8 3.Ne7+ wins.

149) 1.Qxh6+! Kxh6 (1...Kg8 2.Bh4 N(8)h7 3.Nxg6 winning) **2.Nxf7+ Kg7 3.Nxd8** and wins material.

150) 1.Nf6+ Kf7 2.Qxg7+! Kxg7 3.Ne8+! and wins.

151) 1...Rxb1 2.Rxb1 Bxe2 3.Kxe2 Nxc3+ wins the Rb1 after 4.Bxc3 Rxb1.

152) 1...Rxh2+ 2.Kxh2 Nxf3+ 3.K anywhere Nxd2 with two extra pawns.

153) 1...Ne4+! 2.fxe4 Rf8 wins the Queen.

154) 1...Qxg3+ 2.Kxg3 Ne4+ 3.K anywhere Nxd2.

155) 1...Qxe2+! 2.Kxe2 Nxd4+ and 3...Nxf5.

156) 1.Qxc8+ Rxc8 2.Ne6+.

157) 1...Qxf3! 2.gxf3 Ne2+ 3. K moves Nxd4.

158) 1...Nf2+ wins the Queen.

159) 1...Qxd5+! 2.Qxd5 Ne3+ 3. K moves Nxd5 wins a piece.

160) 1...d4! now if the Nc3 moves, then 2...Nb3+ wins the White Queen since the c-pawn is pinned.

161) 1...Nc5 2.Rbb1 Nd3 and 3...Nxf4.

162) 1.Nf6+ Bxf6 2.exf6 and now if 2...Bd7 then 3.Qe3+ wins, since 3...Be6 is forced (3...Kf8 4.Qe7#).

163) 1.fxg8=N! Rxf6+ 2.Nxf6+ K moves 3.Nxd7.

164) 1...Nb3! 2.axb3 (if 2.Rb1 then 2...Nd4 forks Qe2 and Bb5) **2...Qxa1** winning the exchange.

165) 1...Qxd4 2.Qxd4 Nf3+ 3.K moves Nxd4.

166) 1...Rxe4 2.Bxe4 Nc5+ and 3...Nxe4.

167) 1...d2+ 2.Kxd2 Nxe4+ 3.K moves Nxd6.

168) 1...Qxc6 2.Nxc6 Ne2+.

169) 1.Nxe5 Bxe5 (or 1...dxe5 2.Rxc6) **2.Rg8#.**

170) 1...Nh3+ 2.Kg2 (hoping for 2...Rxf3 3.Kxh3) **2...Ng5** wins a piece.

171) 1...N2d4+ 2.cxd4 Nxd4+ 3.K moves Nxc2.

172) 1.Nh7! Qg7 (1...Kxh7 2.Qxh5+ Kg8 (or g7) 3.Qh7#) **2.Nxf8** wins the exchange.

173) 1.Qxg6! fxg6 2.Nf7+ and 3.Nxd8.

174) 1.b5+! and wins, since if 1...Kxb6 2.Nd7+ and 3.Nxf8 or 1...Kxc5 2.Nd7+ again, finally on 1...Kc7 2.Ne6+ wins.

175) 1...Ngf3+! 2.gxf3 Bh4! 3.Qg2 (on 3.Qxh4 comes the fork 3...Nxf3+) **3...Bxe1** winning the exchange.

176) 1.Nf6+! Bxf6 2.Qxg6+ Kh8 3.Qh7#.

177) 1.Rxc6+ Qxc6 2.Ne7+ and 3.Nxc6.

178) 1.Nxf6+ gxf6 2.Rxd4+ wins.

179) 1.b4 Bb6 2.b5 Na5 3.Ne7+.

180) 1.Nxc6 Bxc6 2.Ne7+ K moves 3.Nxc6 wins a pawn plus the exchange.

181) 1.Qxc8 Rxc8 2.Nd7+ K moves 3.Nxb6.

182) 1.Nd8+! Rxd8 2.Qxe7+ and 3.Qxd8.

183) 1...Qxe4 2.Nxe4 Ne2+.

184) 1.Nd5+! The Black c-pawn is pinned.

185) 1.Rh5+! Kf6 (forced, since 1..Bxh5 allows 2.Ne6+ and 3.Nxc7) **2.Rxf5+** followed by 3.Kxg4.

186) 1.Nb6+ cxb6 2.Be6.

187) 1...Nf3+ 2.Kd1 (after 2.Kf1 the same move wins while 2.Ke2 loses the Bishop to 2...Nd4+) **2...e2+ 3.Kxe2 Nd4+** and 4...Nxf5

188) 1.Rxh4! Qxh4 2.Qxf8+! Kxf8 3.Ng6+ and 4.Nxh4.

189) 1...Nxd4 2.Nxc7 Ne2+ 3.Kh1 Nxc1.

190) 1.Rxf8+ Rxf8 2.Rxf8+ Qxf8 3.Nxg6+ and 4.Nxf8.

191) 1.N(either) d6+ Bxd6 2.Nxd6+ Kb8 3.Nxf7.

192) 1.Bxf8 Kxf8 2.Bxf7 Kxf7 3.Nd6+ and 4.Nxc8.

193) 1. Nd6+ Kf8 2.Nxb7.

194) 1.Ne4!! Be8 (1...Rxh5 2.Rxd7+!) **2.Bg5!** and wins.

195) 1.Bxe6+!! and wins! (if 1...Bxe6 2.Qf8+! 2.Kxf8 3.Nxe6+ Ke7 4.Nxc7 Kd6 5.Ne8+).

196) 1.Qxc6 Qxc6 2.Nxe7+ Kh8 3.Nxc6 winning.

CHAPTER 5
DOUBLE ATTACK

197) 1...Bxd5! 2.exd5 g3! 3.hxg3 Qxc4 wins a piece.

198) 1.Bc7 Rxc7 2.Qe5! wins the exchange.

199) 1.Be6!! wins the Black Queen or allows 2.Qg4+ with mate to follow.

200) 1...Rd3! winning the Bc3 since mate by 2...Rh3 is also threatened.

201) 1...c5 2.Nf3 c4 wins a piece.

202) 1...Nxe2+ 2.Qxe2 Qd4+.

203) 1...Qc4! winning either the Rf1 or the Nh4.

204) 1...Nxf3+! 2.gxf3 Qd4+ 3.Kh1 Rxb2.

205) 1...g6 2.Qh4 Bxf4+! 3.Kxf4 g5+.

206) 1...e3 (threatening 2...e2) **2.Re1 exd2** wins a piece.

207) 1...Rd5! 2.Bc4 b5!

208) 1...Nxd5! 2.exd5 Qh4+ and 3...Qxa4.

209) 1.Qd4 f6 2.Nxe4 Rxe4 3.Qxe4 Qxb2 and White has won the exchange.

210) 1...Rxd4! 2.Rxd4 Qe5! threatening mate and the Rd4.

211) 1...Rxe5+! 2.fxe5 Qxe5+ and Qxa1.

212) 1...Qc7+! 2.g3 Qe7! and wins because of the double threat of 3...Qe2# and 3...Qxa3.

213) 1...c6! 2.Bc4 Qa5+ wins the Ne5.

214) 1...Bxh3 2.Kxh3 Qg1 winning a piece.

215) 1...Re8 2.Qf4 Qd4! wins by the attack on both c5 and e3 after 3.Qxd4 Bxd4.

216) 1...Rg3+ picking up the Knight.

217) 1...Qc6! attacking both Ba6 and Rh1.

218) 1...Qe6 2.Qf2 Rxh3+! 3.Kxh3 Qh6#.

219) 1...Rxf2! 2.Rxf2 Nxe4 3.Bxe4 Qxf2+ and mate next.

220) 1...g5 2.Be3 g4.

221) 1.d5! Bxd5 2.Nxf5 and 3.Nxh6.

222) 1...Bc6 spearing both the Nb7 and Rh1.

223) 1...d3! 2.Rxd3 Rxd3 3.Qxd3 e4 wins a piece.

224) 1...Qb6!! (threatening both mate at b2 and the Be3) **2.Bxb6 Ne2#!**

225) 1...Rxb3! 2.axb3 Bd4+.

226) 1.Rxd6! Rxd6 2.Qe5 winning the Rd6 due to the mate threat.

227) 1...Nfxe4 2.Nxe4 Nxe4 3.fxe4 Qh4+ and wins the Bh6 remaining a pawn ahead.

228) 1...Qxd2 2.Rxd2 Bb4 3.Rd1 Rc2.

229) 1.Nxd5! cxd5 2.Qb5+ and 3.Qxb4.

230) 1.Qh8+ Kg5 2.Qe5+ and 3.Qxd5.

231) 1.Rf5 wins either the Ne5 or Bh5.

232) 1...Qxf1+ 2.Kxf1 Bd3+ 3.Ke1 Rf1#.

233) 1.Nxe5 Qxe5 2.Bxd6+.

234) 1.Ne8! Qe7 2.Qg3 Qxe8 3.Qxb8.

235) 1.Rxg7! Kxg7 (or 1...Qxg7 2.Bf6) **2.Bxf6+! Qxf6 3.Nh5+** wins the Queen.

236) 1.d7 Rd8 2.Qa5 wins, since 2...Rb8 fails to 3.d8=Q+.

237) 1.f3 Qh4 2.Qxh4 gxh4 3.e4.

238) 1.Rxe5 fxe5+ 2.Kxe5 and the duel threats of 3.Kxd6 and 3.f6+ win.

239) 1.Qe7+ Kxf5 2.g4+.

240) 1.c6 Rxb6 (1...Rb8 2.Qd6+) **2.Qd8+ and 3.Qxb6.**

241) 1.Nxe5 Rxe5 2.f4.

242) 1.Nh6+! gxh6 2.Qg4+ and 3.Qxe2.

243) 1.d5 Ne7 2.Qa4+!

244) 1.Bxc6 dxc6 (1...Qxc6 makes no difference) **2.Qa3+** and 3.Qxa5.

245) 1.Nxf5 Bxf5 2.Bxf5 Rxf5 3.Qd5+ and 4.Qxa8.

246) 1.Qc7 Rbd8 2.Bxf6 wins, since 2...Rxf6 allows 3.Qxd8+.

247) 1.Nxe5! Nxe5 2.Qh5+ Ng6 3.Qd5 threatening both 4.Qf7# and 4.Qxa8.

248) 1...Rf2!! and wins. (2.Qxe1 Rh2#).

249) 1. Bxf6 Qxf6 2.Qd5+.

250) 1.h3! Nh6 2.Qe4 threatening both 3.Qxc6 and 3.Qxh7#.

251) 1.Rxe4! Rxe4 2.Qc6 wins a Rook.

252) 1.Rxa6 Nxa6 2.Qa4+ and 3.Qxa6 wins two pieces for the Rook.

253) 1.Bxa6 Rxa6 2.Qd3 attacks both the Ra6 and Ng3.

254) 1.Rxg7+ Kxg7 2.Qd4+ and 3.Qxa7.

255) 1. Rxc6+ dxc6 2.Qxc6+ and 3.Qxa8.

256) 1...Qe3! and Black wins. (2.Rxe3 Rh2+ 3.Kg1 Reg2#, or 2.Rxf2 Qxh3+).

257) 1.Ng5 Nf6 (1...Bxg5 2.Qxh7# or 1...Qxd6 then 2.Bxh7+ Kh8 3.Nxf7#) **2.Bxh7+ Kh8 3.Nxf7#.**

258) 1...Qe3! winning. (2.Rxe3 Rf1#; 2.Ra1 Qxg5).

259) 1...Nf3+! winning. (2.gxf3 Qg5+).

260) 1.Qf5 wins, threatening both 2.Qxc8 and mate by 2.Qxh7+ and 3.Qh8.

261) 1.Qc3+ K moves 2.Qe1! wins the Be6 or Rh4.

262) 1.Qe4!

CHAPTER 6
ATTRACTION

263) 1...Bxg5+! 2.Kxg5 f6+ 3.Kg6 (3.Kh4 g5#) **Qg4#.**

264) 1.Nf6!! Kxf6 2.Qf3+ Kg7 3.Qxe4 picking up the Rook.

265) 1.Rh8+! Kxh8 (1...Bxh8 2.Qxg6+) **2.Bxf7 Nh5 3.Qxg6** and wins.

266) 1.Bxf7+ Rxf7 2.Qh8+!! Kxh8 3.Nxf7+ with an extra piece after 4.Nxg5.

267) 1...d4+!! and wins. (2.Qxd4 Nf5+, or 2.Kxd4 Nc6+. If 2.Kf4 Ng6+, or 2.Ke4 Qe2+ 3.Kf4 Ng6+. On 2.Ke4 Qe2+ 3.Kf4 Ng6+ or 3.Kxd4 Nc6+).

268) 1.Qh7+!! Kxh7 2.Nf6+ Kh8 3.Ng6#.

269) 1.Qxg8+ Kxg8 2.Rh8+ Kxh8 3.Bf7#.

270) 1...Ne2+! 2.Kh1 Qxh2+! and wins. (3.Kxh2 Rh4#).

271) 1.Rh8+!! Kxh8 (1...Kf7 2.Qg6+) **2.Qh5+** and wins. (2...Kg8 3.Be6+).

272) 1...Rh1+!! and mate next move.

273) 1.g4+! Kxh4 2.Kg2! and 3.Nf5# cannot be prevented.

274) 1.Qc4+! Qxc4 2.g8=Q+ winning the Black Queen.

275) 1.Re7+!! Qxe7 (1..Kxe7 2.Qxg7+ Ke8 3.Re1+) **2.d6+ Ke8 3.Bb5+** and wins. (3...Kf7 4.dxe7 Nxg4 5.exd8=Q).

276) 1.Qxh6+!! Kxh6 2.hxg6+ Kg7 3.Rh7+ Kg8 4.gxf7+ winning. (4...Rxf7 5.Rc8+).

277) 1.Qd5+!! and wins. (1..Bxd5 2.Bxd5+ Kh8 3.Rxg4).

278) 1.Qg7+!! Kxg7 2.Rfxf7+ and mate in three to follow.

279) 1.Rxh6+! Kxh6 (1...gxh6 2.Rf7+ Kh8 3.Qf5) **2.g4!!** winning. (2...g6 3.Rf7 with 4.Qh3# to follow, and on 3...Kg6 3.Bf7+ Kh6 4.Qh3#).

280) 1...Rxa3+!! and mates!

CHAPTER 7
CLEARANCE

281) 1.Rd8+! (1...Bxd8 2.e7+).

282) 1.Rxd5! (1...exd5 2.e6+).

283) 1...Ra1+! 2.Nxa1 Ba2#.

284) 1.Bd5+! (1...exd5 2.Qh7#).

285) 1.Rxb6! axb6 2.Nf6+ winning. (2...Kf8 3.Qd6+).

286) 1.Qh4! Kg7 2.Nh5+! and wins. (2...gxh5 3.Qf6+ Kf8 4.Ne7#).

287) 1. Rc6+! (1...Bxc6 2.Nc5+ Ka5 3.Bc7#).

288) 1.Qxf5! followed by Ne6+.

289) 1.f3!! Qxf3 2.Qd1! winning. (2...Rxd6 3.Rh2+, or 2...Qh5 3.Rxd8).

290) 1...Qxh7 2.Rxh7 Nd3+ and 3..Nxe1.

291) 1.Bxf7 Rxf7 (1...Qxf7 2.Qd8+) **2.Qh8#.**

292) 1.Re8+! Rxe8 2.Qg4+!! Qxg4 3.Nf6#.

293) 1.Qf6+! Nxf6 2.Bc5+ and wins. (2...Bxc5 3.gxf6+ Kf8 4.Rh8#).

294) 1...Qd1+!! 2.Rxd1 Ne2+!! 3.Bxe2 Nb3#.

295) 1.d5 Qxd5 2.Qh7+ Nxh7 3.Bxh7#.

296) 1...Bg1! 2.Kxg1 Nf3+!

297) 1.g6! Qxg6 (1...Qxf6 2.Qxh7# or 1...hxg6 2.Ng5!) **2.Bxg7 Qxg7 3.Rg1** wins.

298) 1.Ng5! hxg5 2.Qe6+ and 3.Qxc8.

299) 1.d7 Qd8 2.Qd6+ and 3.Qxc5.

300) 1...Rxb4! 2.Nxb4 Bh2+ 3.Kf1 (3.Kh1 Nf2#) **3.Qb6!** and wins.

301) 1.Rxe6+! fxe6 2.Qh5#.

302) 1.Rxd8! Rxc7 2.Rh8+! Kxh8 3.d8=Q+.

303) 1.Qxe5! dxe5 2.Nf6+ and 3.Nxd7.

304) 1...Re6!! and wins. (2.dxe6 Bf2+! 3.Rf2 Rd1+, or 2.Nd2 Qg4+ 3.Kh1 Rxc6 4.dxc6 Qf4).

CHAPTER 8
OVERLOADING

305) 1...Bh3! 2.Re1 (on 2.Nxh3 comes 2...Ne2+) **2...Bg2** winning material.

306) 1...Rxc2!! and White will lose material or be mated on h1.

307) 1.Rxd7! and if 1...Qxd7 2.Bxf6 winning. Obviously 1...Nxd7 is met with 2.Qxg7#.

308) 1...Rf7! winning, as 2.Qxf7 is met with 2...Qg3#. Other White Queen moves leave the Rc3 open to capture.

309) 1.Qh5+! Rxh5 2.Bg6#.

310) 1...Rd4+! 2.Qxd4 Qh2 and 3...Qg3 mates.

311) 1.Rxe5! Qxe5 2.Qf3 Qf6 3.Qd5+ and mate next.

312) 1...Nf5! 2.Nxf5 Rxg2+ and 3...Bxf5.

313) 1...Rxd1+ 2.Rxd1 Qxc3.

314) 1...Re2! threatens mate at h2, while 2.Rxe2 allows 2...Qxf1#.

315) 1...Nf3! threatening 2...Rxf1+! 3.Bxf1 Rxh2#, and the defense 2.Bxf3 allows 2...Rxf1#.

316) 1.Re8! Qxe8 (1...Rxe8 2.Qg7#) **2.Qf6+ Rg7 3.Qxg7#.**

317) 1.Qh6! Bxh6 2.Ne7#.

318) 1...Qd7!! 2.Qc4 (2.Qxd7 Rxf1#) **2...Rxf1+ 3.Qxf1 Qxe6.**

319) 1.Bf6! (threatening 2.Qh6 Nxf6 3.Qh8#) **1...Nxf6 2.Qh8#.**

320) 1...Nxf3+ 2.Qxf3 Bxd2+.

321) 1.Qe5! threatening both the Queen and mate on g7, and 1...Qxe5 loses to 2.Rxf8#.

322) 1.Nd2! d6 (1...Nxd2 2.Rg5#) **2.Nxe4! dxe5** (2...Nxe4 3.Re8#) **3.Nxf6#.**

323) 1...Rxd3! 2.Qxd3 Qxg2#.

324) 1.Bd6! wins since 1...Qxd6 loses to 2.Nxf7#.

325) 1.Re8! Qxe8 2.Qg7#.

326) 1.Qe8! Ka5 (1...Rxg7 2.Qb5#) **2.Qc6! Rxg7 3.Qb5#.**

327) 1.Rh3! Qxh3 2.Qxg7#.

328) 1.Rxc8! Qxc8 2.Qg6 and there is no defense to 3.Qxh6#.

329) 1. Rxh7! wins a piece, since 1...Rxg1 allows 2.Rxh8 and 1...Rxh7 loses to 2.Rxg8.

330) 1.Rxa6! wins, as 1...Rxa6 allows 2.Qd8# and 1...Qxa6 allows 2.Qd7#.

331) 1.Qe7! Qc7 (1...Rxe7 2.Rf8# or 1...Rxf3 2.Qg7#) **2.Qf8+! Rxf8 3.Rxf8#.**

332) 1...Nxf3+ 2.Qxf3 Qxb1+.

333) 1.Qc4! (threatening 2.Qg8#) **1...Rxc4 2.Rxf8#.**

334) 1.Rc8+! Qxc8 2.Qxg7+! Rxg7 3.Rxg7#.

CHAPTER 9
DIVERSION

335) 1.Nxa5! bxa5 2.Nf6+ Ke7 3.Rb7+ winning.

336) 1...Nf3+! and wins. 2.gxf3 is met by 2...Rg6+ 3.Kh1 Nf2#. If 2.Kh1 Nf2# immediately.

337) 1.Nd6! winning. On 1...cxd6 2.Rxe6! (with threats on g7).

338) 1...Ng3+! and wins. On 2.Qxg3 Rxb1 and on 2.hxg3 comes Ra8!! with the devastating Rh8 to follow.

339) 1...Qh4!! and wins. on 2.Nxh4 Rxf2 is mate, and on 2.Kg2 comes 2...Nf4+ 3.Kg1 Qg4+.

340) 1.Rd7! Rb8 (on 1...Bxd7 2.Qxf7+ Rxf7 3.Rxf7#) **2.Nxf7 Bxd7 3.Nd8+.**

341) 1.Bb6!! Qxb6 (1...axb6 2.Qd8#) **2.Qh4+ Rf6** (2...f6 3.Qh7+) **3.Qxb4+** and wins.

342) 1...Rxd4! 2.cxd4 Bb4! 3.Ra3 (g2 must remain protected) **3...Qxa3!** and wins, since on 3.bxa3 comes 3...Bxd2.

343) 1.Ne6! Nxe6 (on 1...fxe6 White mates with 2.Qf8+ Kh7 3.Qh6+ Kg8 4.Rf8#) **2.Qxf7+ Kh8 3.Qxe6** winning easily.

344) 1...Rc2! and wins (2.Qxc2 Nf4+ 3.Kh4 Qg4#).

345) 1.Qe8+! wins (1...Rxe8 2.Bd5+).

346) 1...Rg1+ 2.Kxg1 Qxe2.

347) 1.Re7! Qxe7 2.Qxd5+ picking up the Ra8.

348) 1...Nf3+! 2.Kh1 (on 2.gxf3 Bxd4+ and 3...Qxb5, same for 2.Rxf3) **2...Nxd4 3.Qxc6+ Nxc6** winning a piece.

349) 1...Bxd4 2.Qxb6 Bxb6.

350) 1...Rxg2+ 2.Kxg2 Qxe4+.

351) 1...Nc2+ 2.Qxc2 Qxe2#.

352) 1...Nxe2! 2.Rxb4 (If 2.Kxe2 Qxc3 while 2.Nxe2 allows 2..Qxb1+) **2...Bxc3** and Black emerges a piece ahead.

353) 1...Nc4 2.Rc2 Nxb2 3.Rxb2 Rxc3.

354) 1...Be2! and Black wins the exchange leaving himself two pawns up.

355) 1...Rxd3+ 2.Kxd3 Rxf2.

356) 1.Rxe6! Qxe6 2.Ng5 Qg6 3.Rxh7+ Qxh7 4.Nf7#.

357) 1...Rh1+ 2.Kxh1 Qxf2.

358) 1...Bc2+ 2.Kxc2 Qxe4+.

359) 1...Rb1+! 2.Rxb1 (if 2.Kf2 then 2...Qe1 is mate) **2...Qxa3.**

360) 1...Re3! 2.Qg2 (2.Qxe3 Qh1#) **2...Rxg3.**

361) 1.Nb6 Rb8 2.Nxa8 Rxa8 3.Bxc6.

362) 1...Qd6! 2.Qc3 (if 2.Qxd6 then 2...Rxe1#) **2...Qh2+ 3.Kf1 Qh1#.**

363) 1...Bh4! 2.Qxh4 Qxc2+ and 3...Qxb2.

364) 1.Rd6 Rf6 (1...Re7 2.Nxg6) **2.Nd7** winning the exchange after 2...Bxd7 3.Rxf6.

365) 1.Kg3 Rd4 2.Nf5+.

366) 1...Bxc3 2.bxc3 g5 3.Nd3 Rxe2.

367) 1...Rd2! winning. (2.Qe3 Nc4 3.Qf4 Qxc5).

368) 1...Qxh3+! 2.Nxh3 Nxf3#.

369) 1...Nd4! 2.Nxd4 (on Queen moves, 2...Nxf3+ followed by 3...Qh2#) **2...Qh2#.**

370) 1.Bxf7+! Qxf7 2.Rd8+ Kxd8 3.Qxf7.

371) 1.Qxh7 Rxh7 2.Rf8#.

372) 1.Re1! Rxe1 (1...Kd7 2.Rxe6 Kxe6 3.Qxc6+) **2.Qxc6+ Ke7 3.Qxa8.**

373) 1.Qe6+ Kg7 2.Qe7+ wins the Knight.

374) 1.Qc7! Qxc7 (1...Qd5 2.Bxh6+) **2.Bxh6+ Ke8 3.Rxc7.**

375) 1.Qd8+ Re7 (not 1...Kf5 2.g4#) **2.Nd7+** wins the Rook next move.

376) 1.Qxb4+ Kf5 (1...Ke3 2.Rc3+) **2.Rf6+ Kxf6 3.Qxf4+.**

377) 1.Nd5 Qd8 2.Bxc6 bxc6 3.Nxb4.

378) 1.Rb7+ Kh6 2.Rxh7+ Kxh7 3.Qxf6.

379) 1.Qg4+! Qxg4 2.Rxe8+ Kg7 3.fxg4.

380) 1.Rh4! Nxh4 (1...Qxf6 2.Rhxh7# or 1...Nxg7 2.Qxd6) **2.Qxd6.**

381) 1.Bh3! f6 (on 1...Qxh3 2.Qxd8) **2.Bxd7 fxg5 3.Bxa4.**

382) 1.Qxc6+! Bxc6 2.Nxe6#.

383) 1.Rxe6 Qxe6 2.Bxd5.

384) 1.Rh7+ Kxh7 2.Qxf7+ Kh8 (or h6) **3.Rh1#.**

385) 1.g4! Bg6 2.Nxg6 Nxg6 3.Qxe4.

386) 1...Qxe4+! 2.dxe4 Bf3+ 3.Kg1 Nh3#.

387) 1.Nxc7+ Bxc7 2.Bb5#!

388) 1.Qxg7+!! Nxg7 2.Nh6#!

389) 1.Rxd4! and mate in two follows on any recapture of the Rook.

390) 1.Qc4!! and wins. (1...Qxc4 Rh1mates. If 1...Re7 there follows 2.Qxe4 followed by 3.Rh1+. Finally if the Queen retreats along the h1-a8 diagonal, 2.Qh4+ is allowed).

391) 1.Qa8!! and wins. (Capturing the Queen results in 2. Nxe7+ followed by 3.Nxc8, and on 1...Rb7 2.Nxe7+ Rxe7 3.Qxb8).

392) 1.Qh3! and wins. (1...Qxh3 2.Rxg7+ Kh8 3.Rxf7+ Kg8 4.Rg7+ Kh8 5.Rg8+ and mate).

393) 1...Qa5! and wins. (on 2.Qxa5 Nb3#, or 2.Qd1 Nb3+ 3.Qxb3 Qd2#).

394) 1.Ra8+! and wins. (1...Bxa8 2.Ba6+, or 1...N6b8 2.Rxb8+ Nxb8 3.Rc7#).

395) 1.dxe5 Qxe5 2.Nxd6 Qxd6 3.Bxf4.

396) 1.Qg6!! and wins. (1...fxg6 2.Rxg7+ followed by 3.Nxg6#).

397) 1.Rb1+ Ka7 (1...Kc8 2.Qd7#) **2.Qd4+! Qxd4 3.Nxc6#.**

398) 1...Rxf3! 2.gxf3 Qh3 and mates.

399) 1.Re8! and Black Resigns.

400) 1.Nxf7! and wins. (1...Kxf7 2.Qxg6+ Kf8 3.Qxh6+ Kg8 4.Qh7+ Kf8 5.Bg6 and mate at f7).

401) 1.Rf4+! Kh5 2.Rh4+! gxh4 3.g4#.

402) 1...Qf2+! 2.Qxf2 Rh5+! 3.Bxh5 g5#.

403) 1...Re3+! and wins. (2.fxe3 Qg3#).

404) 1.Rh7+! and wins. (1...Kxh7 2.Qh2+).

405) 1.Rb8!! winning immediately. (1...Qxb8 2.Qxh4!).

406) 1.Nh5!! and wins. (1...Nxh6 2.Qxh6 Rg8 3.Rf7).

407) 1.Ncd6! and wins. (if 1...exd6 2.Nf6+, or 1...Qxb2 2.Nf5 Qxc1+ 3.Bf1 Qe3+ 4.Kh1!)

408) 1...Bf3!! winning. (2.gxf3 Rh6 3.Re1 Qxh2+ 4.Kf1 Qh3+ 5.Kg1 Qh1#, or 2.Qd3 Rh6 3.h3 Bxg2, or 2.g3 Qxh2+!).

409) 1...Qf3!! and wins (2.gxf3 Nexf3+ 3.Kh1 Bh3 with mate coming on g2).

CHAPTER 10
BACK RANK

410) 1...Rxd6! 2.Qxd6 (2.exd6 Qe1+ and wins) **2...Rd8** and wins. If 3.Qxe7 then 3...Rd1#.

411) 1...Qxg2+! 2.Rxg2 Rb1+ 3.Rg1 R (either) xg1#.

412) 1...Qd4+ 2.Kh1 Qf2! and wins, since 3.Rxf2 allows 3...Re1+ and mate next, while if 3.Qb5, then 3...Re1 wins.

413) 1.Qxc7+! Rxc7 2.Rxd8+ Rc8 3.R (either) xc8#.

414) 1...Rc5! and now if 2.Rxc5 then 2...Qxb7. If instead 2.dxc5, then 2.Qd1#.

415) 1...Bxe4! and if 2.Qxe4, then 2...Qf1+ mating, while if 2.Rxe4, then again Qf1+ mates.

416) 1...Rc1! 2.Rxc1 Qd1+! 3. Rxd1 Rxd1#.

417) 1...f3+! 2.Kg1 Qxf1+! 3.Kxf1 Rd1#.

418) 1...b5! 2.Qxc6 Qf1+ 3.Rxf1 Rxf1#.

419) 1.Qxa8! Rxa8 2.Rd8+ Rxd8 3.Rxd8#.

420) 1.Rxb8+! Kxb8 2.Qxe5+! and if 2...fxe5, then 3.Rf8+ mates.

421) 1.Qxd6! cxd6 2.Nf7+ Kg8 (if 2...Rxf7 then 3.Re8+ mates) **3.Nxg5** and wins.

422) 1.Qxf6+ Rxf6 2.Rd8+ Rf8 3.Rxf8#.

423) 1.Nf5! Rd7 (if 1...exf5, 2.Rd8+ mates next) **2.Bxd7** and wins material.

424) 1.Rxe5! Nxe5 (if 1...Qxc4, then 2.Re8#) **2.Qc8+ Qd8 3.Qxd8#.**

425) 1.Qc3! Qc5 (if 1...Qxc3, then 2.Rxf8 is mate) **2.Rxf8+ Qxf8 3.Qxb2** and wins.

426) 1.Qb3+ Kh8 2.Qf7! wins, since 2...Rxf7 allows 3.Rxe8 and mate next.

427) 1.Qc4+ Kh8 (if 1...Rf7, then 2.d7 Qd2 3.Rad1 and wins) **2.Qxg4!** and wins, since 2...fxg4 allows 3.Rxf8#.

428) 1.Qxb4 axb4 2.Rxa8+ Be8 3.Bxd5! and if 3...Qxd5, then 4.Rxe8#.

429) 1.Rxe8 Qxe8 2.Qa4! and wins, as 2...Qxa4 allows 3.Rb8+ forcing mate.

430) 1...Qg2+! 2.Qxg2 Rxe1+ 3.Qf1 Rxf1#.

431) 1.Qc6! (threatening 2.Ra8#) **1...Qxc6 2.dxc6 Kb8 3.Rfa1** and mate by 4.Ra8 cannot be stopped.

432) 1...Nd3+ 2.Qxd3 Qc1+ 3.Rxc1 Rxc1#.

433) 1...Qe4!! and White resigns as the Black Queen is diverted from pinning the Rook on f7.

434) 1.Rc8! Rxc8 2.Qd8+ Rxd8 3.Rxd8#.

435) 1...Rgc8! and White Resigns. The Rook on c1 cannot be defended, and if it moves along the first rank, there comes ...Qxa1!! winning.

436) 1...Ng4! 2.Qxd6 1.Rf1#.

437) 1...Qd2! attacking both Queen and Rook, and 2.Qxd2 allows 2...Rf1#.

438) 1...Ne4! 2.fxe4 Rxd1#, or if 2.Qxa7, Rxd1#.

439) 1...Qe4! and if 2.Qe2, then 2...Qxe2 3.Rxe2 Rxd1+ and mate next or if 2.Qxe4 then 2...Rxd1+ mates.

440) 1...Qxe4! and if 2.Qxd6, then 2...Qe1#, while 2.dxe4 allows 2...Rd1+ and mate next.

441) 1...Qd6! 2.Rxd6 Re1+ 3.Kh2 Rh1#.

442) 1...Qb2! 2.Rd3 (if 2.Qd3 Qa1+! wins, but not 2...Rxd3 allowing 3.Rc8+ mating. Also if 2.Qxb2 Rd1#) **2...Qb1+** and wins.

443) 1...Qe2!! and if 2.Rdxe2 Nxe2+ 3.Rxe2 Rf1#, or if 2.Nf6+ Rxf6 3.exf6 Qxd2 wins a piece.

444) 1...Rxa3!! and wins, since 2.Qxa3 allows mate after 2...Qe1+ and 2.Rxa3 again fails against 2...Qe1+. Finally, if 2.bxa3, then 2...Qxa1+ 3.Qb1 (or 3.Rb1) and 3...Re1+ mates.

CHAPTER 11
MIXED THEMES

445) 1...d4! 2.Qxd4 Qxb3#.

446) 1...c5! 2.Nde2 (2.Nc2 Nxf3+ 3.gxf3 Bxc3) **2...Nxc4** wins a pawn.

447)1...Rd3! 2.Qxd3 (2.Bxd3 Qxh3+ 3.Kg1 Qg2#) **2...Nxd3 3.Bxd3 Qd6+** and 4...Qxd3.

448) 1...Ne2+ 2.Bxe2 (2.Rxe2 Qxg4) **2...Qxe3+ and 3...fxg4.**

449) 1.Ne4! Bxe4 2.Rxe4 dxe4 3.Qg3#.

450) 1...Bd6!! 2.Rxd6 (2.Bxd6 d1=Q) **h2** and queens a pawn.

451) 1.Rd5! exd5 (1...Qxd5 2.Qf6#) **2.Qxd8+ Re8 3.Qxe8#.**

452) 1...Ng4+! followed by 2...Be5+ wins the White Queen.

453) 1.Re3! Bxe3 2.Qxg7#.

454) 1.Ne6! and 2.Qxh6#.

455) 1...Nf3+ 2.gxf3 Qxd1+ wins.

456) 1.Qxg6+ fxg6 2.f7+ Qxf7 3.Rh8#.

457) 1...Bd3+! 2.Qxd3 Qxg1+.

458) 1.Rg3+ Kf7 2.Qxf4+.874) 1.Rf5! exf5 2.Qxh5#.

459) 1.Rf5! exf5 2.Qxh5#.

460) 1.Bxg6!! and wins.

461) 1.Bd6! Rxd6 (1...Qxb3 2.Rf8#) **2.Qxb8+** mates in two.

462) 1.Qa2+! Bxa2 2.Rb2+! Kxc1 3.Rxf2 wins.

463) 1.Rf3! Rd5 2.Rc8! and wins.

464) 1...Rc4+ 2.Kd2 Rc1! winning. (3.Kxc1 h2 and promotes).

465) 1...Qxf3+ 2.Kxf3 Ne3! and wins. (3.Kxe3 h2).

466) 1.Qxc8+! Nxc8 2.d7 and queens next.

467) 1...Bb2! 2.Nxb2 c1=Q+ and wins.

468) 1...b2! 2.Qc3 Bb4! 3.Qxb4 Nxb4 and 4...bxa1=Q.

469) 1.Rxg4! Rxg4 2.e7 Rg8 3.Rd8 and wins.

470) 1...Re1! 2.Rxe1 Nxe1 3.Kxe1 h2 and queens.

471) 1.e8=Q+! Kxe8 2.Ba4 wins.

472) 1...Ra3+ 2.Kc2 Rxf3! 3.gxf3 h3 and queens in two.

473) 1.Qxb6! axb6 2.Nxc6 and the a-pawn will be decisive.

474) 1...Rxh7! 2.Rc1 (The Rook cannot be captured) **2...Kc3** and wins.

475) 1...Qxf1+! 2.Qxf1 Re1+.

476) 1...Rxc2! 2.Nxc2 Qf1+ 3.Ka2 b1=Q#.

477) 1...Qxh2! 2.Rxh2 gxh2 and queens next.

478) 1.Qxd5! cxd5 2.a6 and queens in two more moves.

479) 1.Qxd6+! Qxd6 2.c7 and wins.

480) 1.Ne3! Nd6 (1...Nxe3 2.Rc8+) **2.Rc8+!! Nxc8 3.Rxb8 Nxb8** and 4.bxc8=Q+.

481) 1...d2! and now 2.Rd1 Qxe6 or 2.Qxd7 dxe1=Q#.

482) 1.Qxe6 Qxe6 2.d7+.

483) 1...Qxd1 2.Qxd1 a1=Q winning.

484) 1.Qg8+ Kd6 2.Ba3+ Kc6 3.Qa8+ wins the Black Queen.

485) 1.Ra1+ Kb8 2.Ra8+ Kc7 3.Ra7+.

486) 1.Rxe5 dxe5 2.Rd1+.

487) 1.Rh8 Rxa7 2.Rh7+ wins the Rook.

488) 1...Qa2! (threatening 2...Qa1#) **2.c3 Bf3** winning the exchange.

489) 1.Ne5+ Ke6 2.Qg8+.

490) 1...Nxc4 2.Qxc4 Be6 wins the exchange.

491) 1...Bg4 2.Qd2 Bxd1.

492) 1...Ra4+! 2.bxa4 b4#.

493) 1...Rc1+! 2.Kxc1 Re1+! 3.Nxe1 Qxe1#.

494) 1...Na4! 2.bxa4 (2.Kxa4 Ra1#) **2...Rxb6.**

495) 1.Rg6! fxg6 2.hxg6+ Rxg6 3.fxg6+ winning.

496) 1...Bg4 wins the piece since 2.Ng1 is met by 2...f3, and 2.Qd1 loses to 2...Nd4.

497) 1.Bh6+! Kxh6 2.Qd2+ followed by 3.Nxd8 winning the Black Queen.

498) 1.Nxe6 fxe6 2.Rxe6+! Qxe6 3.Nxg7+ and 4.Nxe6.

499) 1.Bxc6+! Kxc6 2.Qb7#.

500) 1...g5! 2.Bg3 g4 3.Ng1 Bxg2.

501) 1...Nh4! wins the Queen.

502) 1.Ne3 wins the Queen.

503) 1.Nf4 wins the Queen.

504) 1.Qf7+! Nxf7 2.exf7#.

505) 1...c5 2.Qe3 c4.

506) 1.f6+ hxg4 2.Be6+ Ke8 3.f7#.

507) 1.Rad1 Bxg4 2.Rd3#.

508) 1.Qh6+ Nxh6 2.Bxh6#.

509) 1...Qf1+! 2.Bg1 Qf3+!! 3.Bxf3 Bxf3#.

510) 1.Qxe4+! Nxe4 2.Bxf7#.

511) 1.Qxd7+! Nxd7 2.Ne6#.

512) 1...g5 2.Bg3 h5 3.Nh2 h4 wins the Bg3.

513) 1...Qxh4+ 2.Kg1 Qh1+ 3.Kf2 Qh2+ and **4...Qxc2.**

514) 1.Qg4! g6 2.Qd4 and mate at g7 or h8 next.

515) 1.c6! bxc6 2.Ba6+ Kd8 3.Qb8#.

516) 1.Qh8+ Kxe7 2.Re1+ Kd6 3.Qe5#.

517) 1.Qa6 bxa6 2.Rb8#.

518) 1.Qxh6! gxh6 2.Bh7#.

519) 1...Qg1+! 2.Rxg1 Nf2#.

520) 1.Qxf6+! Kxf6 2.Be5#.

521) 1.Qh6 and **2.Qg7#.**

522) 1.Nxf6! Bxf6 2.Qxh7+! Kxh7 3.Rh5#.

523) 1.Rxg7! Rxg7 2.Qxh6+ Rh7 3.Qxf8#.

524) 1.Qg4+ Qg6 2.Ne7+ and **3.Nxg6.**

525) 1.h6+ Kg8 2.Qf6 and **3.Qg7#.**

526) 1...Nd7 2.Bxd4 exd4 and **3...Nb6#** is unstoppable.

527) 1.Qxf8+! Kxf8 2.e7#.

528) 1.Rh7+! Kxh7 2.Qxf7+ Kh8 3.Rh1+ mating.

529) 1.Qxh7+ Rxh7 2.Rg8#.

530) 1...Bb4+! 2.axb4 Qe3+ 3.Kc2 Nxb4#.

531) 1.Ne6! Bxe6 2.Qh7+! Kxh7 3.Rh3#.

532) 1...Nd4+ 2.Ke3 Nef5#.

533) 1.Rxh7! Kxh7 2.Qh5+ Kg8 3.Bxg6 and wins quickly.

534) 1...Qxd1+!! 2.Qxd1 Bg4! 3.Qxd8+ (If the Queen moves, then 3...Rd1+) **3...Nxd8** with an extra piece.